Encounters With Stuff

Adventures of a Chemist

by
Gordon Van Praagh

Pentland Books
Edinburgh – Cambridge – Durham – USA

First published in 2001 by
Pentland Books Ltd
1 Hutton Close
South Church
Bishop Auckland
Durham
manuscripts@pentlandpress.co.uk
sales@pentlandpress.co.uk
www.pentlandpress.co.uk

ISBN 1–85821-888–8

Typeset in Palatino 13 on 15 by
Carnegie Publishing
Carnegie House
Chatsworth Road
Lancaster
www.carnegiepub.co.uk

Printed and bound by
Antony Rowe Ltd
Chippenham

Encounters With Stuff

CONTENTS

PREFACE

How pleasant to know Mr Lear
Who has written such volumes of stuff
(Edward Lear)

IN COLLOQUIAL CONVERSATION we use the word 'stuff' to apply to dress-making material, foodstuffs and in fact to almost any kind of substance. As a chemist, I would also refer to all chemicals as 'stuff'.

My late colleague and mentor, Frank Halliwell, Professor of Chemical Education in the University of East Anglia, nearly always referred to chemicals as 'stuff' – 'that blue stuff in the bottle ... don't get that corrosive stuff on your skin ... do you know that this stuff has a very complex structure?', and so on. We all use the word: 'What beautiful stuff your curtains are made of'; 'I wonder what sort of stuff gives that butterfly's wings such brilliant colours?'

All these stuffs are composed of chemicals and yet, when the word 'chemical' is used, most people think of substances such as disinfectants, fertilisers, pesticides etc, and view chemists and the chemical industry as being involved in making only these. In fact, the industry is mainly concerned with manufacturing substances that are essential to modern life and in producing improved materials that will enhance the quality of our lives.

All materials are made of chemicals, yet the public image

of chemistry is unfriendly. In this book I have tried to take the fear out of the word 'chemical' by discussing some useful substances such as paper, oil and foodstuffs, which, like all other materials, are made up of chemicals. With an almost infinite number of 'stuffs' to choose from, I have selected only those about which I can relate some personal experience or happening.

> We live in a world made of stuff.
> I have chosen some bits – just enough
> Which I'll use to display
> In a light-hearted way
> That Chemistry's fun – and not tough.

A.L.M.

I acknowledge my indebtedness to Primo Levi, author of *The Periodic Table*. His book gave me the idea for the format of mine. He uses the name of an element, e.g. gold, carbon etc, as the title for each chapter and these are used as pegs on which to hang experiences from the author's life. In my book, the names of elements are replaced by various 'stuffs'. In addition to some discussion of the chemistry of the stuff, I relate personal encounters with it which I hope the reader will find interesting or amusing.

Gordon Van Praagh

ACKNOWLEDGMENTS

I HAVE HAD MUCH HELP from friends, especially John Churchman, who helped me when I needed information by finding it on the Internet, Tony Mansell whose critical eye helped me to avoid making errors, small or disastrous, and Fiona Potter whose skill and patience was stretched to the limit in typing and re-typing my only-just-legible scripts. I am most grateful to the staff of the Pentland Press who have been very helpful at every stage of the publishing process, also to Michael Guest, to whose skills the colour photographs and front cover are an eloquent testimony. Charles and Mary Kirkman helped me with their faultless proof-reading. I am also grateful to Martin Berry, Education Consultant to the Royal Society of Chemistry, and to the Association for Science Education for their help and encouragement. Lance Reynolds and Jack Doyle were also very supportive

I am very grateful to the DuPont company, USA for their interest and financial support.

CHAPTER 1: INK

Still essential in spite of computers

With a single drop of ink for a mirror, the Egyptian sorcerer undertakes to reveal to any chance comer far-reaching visions of the past. This is what I undertake to do for you, Reader. With this drop of ink at the end of my pen I will show you the roomy workshop of Mr Jonathan Burge, carpenter and builder in the village of Hayslope, as it appeared on the eighteenth of June, in the year of our Lord, 1799.

(George Eliot *Adam Bede*, 1859)

MY EARLIEST RECOLLECTION OF INK was in a specially shaped bottle so designed that it could be filled from the top, yet when it was laid on its side or inverted, no ink spilled out. I was a schoolboy at the time and the bottle was on a table in our Headmaster's study. He was teaching Scripture to about a dozen of us who were seated round a large oval table with the inkpot near the edge. It was our objective to tip the table a little, using our knees, and to get the inkpot to roll all the way round before the Headmaster noticed. As far as I recall, he never did.

When I was teaching, I knew that my pupils would not remember much, if anything, of what I had said. They said (like the Red King in *Alice through the Looking Glass*): 'I shall never, never forget', but, as the Red Queen replied: 'You will, though, if you don't make a memorandum of it.' Later in the book, Lewis Carroll writes:-

> In Winter when the fields are white
> I sing this song for your delight.
> In Spring when leaves are getting green,
> Perhaps I'll tell you what I mean.
> In Summer when the days are long,
> Maybe you'll understand my song.
> In Autumn when the leaves are brown,
> Take pen and ink and WRITE IT DOWN.

According to the Oxford dictionary ink is a 'fluid for writing with a pen'. Ink does not consist of a single stuff but is a mixture of several substances. According to the *Encyclopaedia Britannica*, 'Writing inks are solutions of colouring material and other substances in water. The first inks, dating from 2500 BC and used in the Egyptian and Chinese civilisations, were made of lampblack ground with a solution of gum.' Chinese people used a block of solid ink. This they moistened and used with a fine paint brush for writing the

After Tenniel

Chinese characters. Some still do.

Lampblack consists largely of the element carbon. It is still used in 'Indian ink' to give the black colour. Many coloured juices and extracts have been used as inks, 'including dragon's blood, alizarin, indigo, pokeberries, cochineal and sepia.' So now we know!

The basis of modern blue-black inks is ferrous sulphate plus tannin. Ferrous sulphate (now known as 'iron II sulphate') is undoubtedly a 'chemical'. But what about tannin? It was obtained by treating oak galls with hot water, but now pure gallic and tannic acids are used. The following substances, all of which we would call 'chemicals', are used in making coloured inks: tri-phenyl-methane, azines, thiazine and anthraquinone. So it is quite clear that this common stuff 'ink' consists of chemicals – a useful and harmless stuff produced by chemists.

However, ink is not always entirely harmless. An elderly lady whom I once knew lived above the pub in a nice Sussex village. Every morning she was to be seen in the sitting room wearing a pair of white gloves while she read the *Daily Telegraph*. They did not remain white because the carbon black used for printing the paper came off to a small extent. The better the quality of the paper used, the less does the carbon black adhere to it. These days diluted bitumen is used as an adhesive (no doubt because it is cheaper than gum) and sticks better to porous paper than to higher-quality papers. (Can this be why *The Times* is cleaner than *The Telegraph*?).

One might think that modern communications by telephone, fax, etc do not require the use of ink, but of course this is not so. For a fax, the message has first to be written, printed or drawn. Although a modern computer can be used to make elaborate designs in many colours, sooner or later such designs have to be reproduced using a printer. This can accurately reproduce high-definition print and graphics, but for this purpose special inks had to be developed. The story is as follows.

In an ordinary ink the dye has to be sufficiently soluble to prepare a solution concentrated enough to produce a visible mark on paper. These 'marks' will smudge unless blotted or given time to dry. Ink-jet printers also require a dye with a higher solubility. This causes a major problem with a mechanical printer because the print it produces must not smudge at all. The ideal answer would be a dye with a high solubility in water at the print-head but zero solubility on the printed page. In trying to develop an ink with these properties, chemists decided to start with a black dye-stuff called 'Food Black II' and modify it. This dye had been used for many years as a food-colouring for liquorice, wine gums etc. The problem was that Food Black II, although it has a high solubility, smudges badly on paper. So chemists worked on modifying its molecular structure so that, while it retained its high solubility, this changed when the ink came into contact with the paper. To bring off this clever trick, the research workers first studied the chemistry of paper. They found that paper is usually slightly acidic. They then tried to use this fact to reduce the solubility of the dyestuff when it contacted the paper. They were able to make a small change in the molecular structure of Food Black II so that the acid in the paper converted it to a nearly insoluble substance that did not smudge.

Please refer to the Glossary for the chemical formulae of these substances. The molecule of Food Black II has lost three of its $Na^+ SO^-_3$ groups and the molecule of Ink Jet Black has an additional two $Na^+ CO^-_2$ groups.

So the modern stuff we talk of as 'just ink' continues to be the subject of research by chemists, and the relation between ink and paper has become even more important.

Bernard Levin, my favourite essayist, discusses problems that arise from NOT 'writing it down'. He points out that when he uses a computer the words he 'writes' are stored automatically as electrical impulses. They can of course be printed out at the touch of a button. 'Supposing that Beethoven had had a music computer and had written his three overtures to Fidelio on it, we might never have known about the earlier versions.' He could have written Leonora No.1 and, wanting to replace it with Leonora No.2, could have stored No.1 in the computer's memory, but he might not have done so – he might have been so dissatisfied as to 'wipe' it off. The same fate might have befallen Leonora No.2 after he wrote No.3. 'I don't trust this world – I fear that one day I shall wake up and find that the last bottle of ink has been emptied.' (*B.L.*)

A writer who wanted to think
Said I really can't do without ink.
My thoughts go astray
And seem far away
Till I put them on paper with ink.

G.V.P.

CHAPTER 2: PAPER

I ONCE SAW PRETTY GIRLS in Thailand making a primitive kind of paper. They were using the oldest method on record. Old bits of cloth were used as the source of fibres. These were first broken down by being crushed in water until the cotton fibres of which they had been made formed a loose pulp in the water. The girls then used a one-metre square of wire gauze fixed to a wooden frame, immersing it in the tank containing the water and pulp. They then very skilfully lifted it up in a horizontal position, removing a layer of tangled fibres. The frame was then tilted into a slanting position and left to dry in the sun (*photograph*). The 'rag-paper' that resulted was of poor quality, not suitable for writing on – but rather good as a wrapping paper.

Rag paper first became available to the rest of the world in the eighth century, the art having been learnt from the Chinese by the Arabs. The first mention of rag-paper in Europe occurs in a tract of Peter, Abbot of Cluny, in the middle of the twelfth century. The oldest known use in Europe of 'oriental paper' was for a charter in 1228 by Frederick II, but in 1231 he forbade the further use of paper for public documents, which were to be inscribed on vellum.

Before the invention of paper became widely known in Europe, vellum was used for writing on. What is vellum? The *Encyclopaedia Britannica* answers: 'Skins of certain animals have supplied writing material on which has been inscribed the literature of centuries. The delicate skins of newly born calves or lambs came to be generally known as vellum'. Improvement in the treatment of animal skins resulted in a smoother, thinner material, both sides of which could be used for writing on. This material came to be known as parchment. We know from Roman authors that vellum was competing with paper as a writing material as early as the second century AD.

But, as the second millennium approached, vellum almost fell from grace. Since 1850 all Acts of Parliament have been printed on vellum. But the latest report from the Record Office in the House of Lords said that vellum (made, in Parliament's case, from goatskin) tended 'to be oily and smelly. It is not attractive stuff to come into contact with. It is increasingly scarce and expensive and one A4 page costs £28'. Consideration was given to replacing vellum by a special paper with a life expectancy of 250 years. But vellum has been reprieved, Parliament voting to uphold tradition and its historic connections with the tiny vellum-making industry, which might otherwise have been endangered.

Another type of paper is made from the stems of the 'paper reed', *Cyprus papyrus*, a plant which is a member of the sedge family. The use of papyrus for making writing materials dates back to the Egyptians. Papyrus rolls are represented in Egyptian wall paintings and many examples of the rolls themselves are extant. The Greeks also used papyrus for literary purposes as early as the 5th century BC and it was later used in Italy as a vehicle for Roman literature. Under the Empire its use became extensive for correspondence and legal documents. In the reign of Tiberius, because of the failure of the papyrus crop, 'there was a danger of the ordinary business of life being deranged.' (*Enc. Brit.*).

Wood is now widely used in the manufacture of paper. The widespread destruction of woodland and forests to provide wood for the paper industry is a menace to the welfare of the environment in many places. There are other objections: the bleaching of the wood pulp involves the use of a number of chemicals. This treatment removes a variety of constituents and leaves a material consisting largely of cellulose, but the substance used to bleach the paper, namely chlorine, reacts with the cellulose to produce poisonous organic chlorides and the disposal of the waste water gives rise to serious pollution. To reduce this, chemical technologists have introduced the use of bleaching agents that are much less harmful than chlorine.

I first became aware of the significance of 'logging' when driving up towards the central hills of Malaysia. The tree-lined road was almost free of traffic except for the occasional lorry coming towards us loaded with three enormous tree trunks – all it had space for. We kept passing more and more lorries, so I began to count them. After over 100, I gave up. Later, we stopped for curry and rice with a Chinese 'tokay'. The photo gives some idea of the size of one of these 'logs' (*photograph*).

Not many years later, I heard the Federal Minister, Stephen Yong, justifying the cutting down of these ancient trees. He spoke of seeing the operation in the light of the modernisation of industries in Malaysia. He countered the criticism that de-forestation was destroying the habitat of the oldest people of Malaysia – the Punans. They wanted a higher standard of living. Directly a few individuals had experienced the outside world, they returned home with glowing accounts of better food, modern medicine, even cinemas, and it was not long before they no longer wanted to live in the jungle.

I once met Stephen Yong and his wife at a cocktail party in his home in Kuching, Sarawak, in 1960, before Independence. I remember Mrs Yong offering me prawn cocktail while telling me that they were happy 'under the British' and had even written to the Queen asking her not to give them Independence. They had seen the trouble that was arising in Africa as various states became independent. Only a few years later, Sarawak (with Sabah) was grouped with West Malaysia as the independent new nation of Malaysia.

Agricultural and forestry experts are well aware of the threats to the world's forests. The use of soft woods such as poplar for replanting is helping to alleviate some of them. The poplars have a weaker kind of lignin which is easier to separate from the cellulose, thus reducing the need for chemicals in paper production. The use of G.M. (genetically modified) poplar trees could cut the cost of making paper by a fifth. There is no risk of cross-pollination from these G.M. trees as those grown for paper-making are all female.

Huge amounts of paper are manufactured annually, over 250 million tons worldwide. This weight of paper is three times the weight of the annual production of motor cars. An enormous amount of water is used to make all this paper. It takes about 80 gallons to make the paper for one Sunday newspaper. Most of the water is used early in the process for floating the fibres into uniform layers. This mixture is passed over wire grills and much of the water drained off. A sheet of fibres is then passed between rollers and most of the water remaining is squeezed out. The last step in the process is to pass the damp sheets over heated rollers. It is here that chemical bonds are formed between the cellulose molecules and these hold the finished sheet of paper together.

However, paper made only of cellulose would be too soft and weak for most purposes and so it usually requires the inclusion of other substances such as 'fillers', dyes and resins, but the bulk of paper consists of cellulose. The properties of cellulose, like those of any other substance, are a consequence of its internal structure. The fibrous contents of paper suggest that its structure consists of long molecules and this is indeed the case. In fact, cellulose particles consist of chains of carbon atoms which, in places, are joined to hydrogen and oxygen atoms and other short chains of carbon atoms (for formula, see *Glossary*).

Together with myriads of other similar molecules this formula represents the structure of cellulose. Have you ever noticed that when you cut out a section from a newspaper using a paper-knife or a pair of scissors, the paper tears easily downwards but not across? When the paper was rolled out during manufacture, the cellulose molecules were lined up in one direction and it is easily split along this direction. But the molecules object strongly to being sliced across their length.

The formula reflects not only the fibrous nature of cellulose, but also its property of absorbing water and swelling up to form a pulp. It does this because the -OH groups in its structure have a strong attraction for water. The water molecules attach themselves to the -OH groups and when this happens all over the cellulose 'chains', they swell up and become a pulp. Halfway through World War II, a week before I reported for duty at the Admiralty Department of Scientific Research, they had had a command from the Prime Minister, Winston Churchill, to produce paper that would dissolve in water. This strange order arose because secret papers had been lost when one of our ships had been torpedoed. If the paper had dissolved in the sea, the secrets would have been safe. My colleagues considered the P.M.'s idea and did not think much of it! Suppose a wave splashed over the secret orders or the Commander spilt his gin and tonic over them? They therefore replied saying that the project was not practicable. The response was not long in coming. I saw it myself, signed 'W.S.C.'. It read: 'To the scientist all things are possible – produce it in a month'. They did, and I kept several specimens for some years afterwards. It was made from seaweed. If you threw a piece of the paper into a bowl of water, it spread out over the surface of the water and you could stir it in like milk. However, the paper became soggy in moist air and brittle in dry air. So, as my colleagues had said in the first place, the project was not practicable.

By far the most important use of paper is in making

books. I recently visited a printing factory where stacks of paper were printed on in black and white or colour by the most modern photographic process. Cut by powerful guillotines that could slice a pile of paper several inches thick, the resultant pages were neatly sewn into book form. The spine was then glued with gum arabic and enclosed in hardback covers made by hand on the spot. Where was this factory, equipped with the latest Italian and German machinery, situated? In Wapping, London? No. It was in a charming Malay village called Kampong Serenok (Serenok=Happy) within 10 minutes' drive into the countryside from Penang airport. The single-storey buildings snaked their way from the country road into the village until they led to the most beautiful kampong I have ever seen. Malay-style wooden houses on stilts were well spaced along the village paths, themselves lined with a variety of tall palm trees and generously planted with bougainvillaeas. A more unlikely situation for a modern printing works would be hard to imagine. So impressed was the State Governor when he visited the factory during its early days, that he created the founder a Malaysian knight (*Dato*) on the spot!

Paper, as well as being essential in making books, notepads and unwanted advertising material, has also other uses. It is still used for doing up parcels and lining shelves – although threatened by other less attractive materials made of various types of plastic. Around 1920 a firm called Marshall Lloyd made and sold chairs made of paper – not toys but chairs one could sit on. They produced over 1,000 designs in many colours. In the 1990's a pair of chairs made of paper cost about £700. It is now quite common for people to wear disposable underwear, also made of paper.

These days we think of paper as essential for writing and printing on. What would schools do without it? Well, some have had to manage. A Burmese friend of mine told me that until recent times, Buddhist monks in Burma made copies of their scriptures by a traditional method, using neither paper nor ink. The elegantly curved characters were cut into the surface of long strips of palm leaf using a sharp stylus; the writing went along the strip of leaf so that only a few lines could be fitted in on each strip. The strips were then strung together so that the completed book was like a venetian blind.

Few people will remember using slates for writing on at school. I once visited a secondary school in Lesotho (when it was Basutoland). The school was high up in the central hills of the country and as we approached it in our jeep, we passed a couple of large mud huts outside which a group of children was sitting. It was a primary school. The teacher was standing by a slate black-board which was perched on a wooden trestle and the pupils each had a bit of slate (of various shapes) on which they seemed to make notes with a piece of hard rock. Maybe we should show more appreciation of our paper and ink!

> If all the earth were paper white
> And all the sea were ink
> 'Twere not enough for me to write
> As my poor heart doth think.
>
> (*John Lely* 1554–1606)

There was an eccentric old draper
Who used to make clothes out of paper
But the girls, when they wore them
Invariably tore them
You never did see such a caper.

G.V.P.

CHAPTER 3: WATER

The most wonderful substance in the world

M Y OLD YORKSHIRE FRIEND, Joe Bradley, was someone who really appreciated the uniqueness of water. I can see him now as he stands in front of his class teaching chemistry. Dressed in his brown lab. coat, with a test-tube of colourless liquid in his hand, he is measuring its boiling point with a thermometer. With a broad smile on his moon-like face, he is saying: 'One hundred degrees! – it's water, the most wonderful substance in the world!' – pronouncing it in a strong Yorkshire accent. Of course he was right.

Water is remarkable not only for its abundance on earth and the multifarious uses it has, but also for its unique properties. It differs from any other liquid in several ways. All these exceptional properties are due to its structure – to its formula being H_2O – two atoms of hydrogen joined to one atom of oxygen. If there is a chemical formula that is familiar to the layman, it is surely this formula, H_2O. Yet it took the chemists of the early 19th century many years of experimenting and theorising to arrive at this conclusion. The concept of an atom goes back to the Greek philosophers, Democritus and Leucippus, to whom an atom was the smallest part of a substance which could exist. Today this definition is more applicable to a molecule of a substance, molecules being composed of a few atoms, either all the same or a group of different atoms, as in H_2O. Very few substances exist as single atoms – helium, neon and argon are examples. Most substances exist as molecules. You can have a balloon full of hydrogen molecules (H_2) but not of hydrogen atoms (H).

The word 'molecule' refers to the smallest particle of any pure substance that could have a separate existence. We now know that the formula of water is H_2O, but John Dalton, who formulated his atomic theory in 1808, wrote the formula of water as HO. It was not until about 1858 that chemists concluded that H_2O was the true formula of water. (Don't ask me how – if you want to know, you must consult a textbook on the history of chemistry – most ordinary school chemistry textbooks do not explain it; they take it for granted.) I was discussing this subject while walking along the wooded cliffs looking out on the surf as it rolls in from the deep blue seas along the coastal bays of New South Wales. My companion, Paul Mckeown, had been Headmaster of Canberra Grammar School and President of the Independent Schools Conference of Australia. No-one could accuse him of being an ignorant man, yet he did not understand what 'H_2O' meant. He wasn't sure if it symbolised two atoms of oxygen with one of hydrogen or vice versa. I tried to explain, but found myself having to define the words 'molecule' and 'atom' and distinguish between them. So when I came to write this chapter, I thought I should devote a few paragraphs to H_2O.

Water differs from all other liquids in a number of ways and these differences are all due to the structure of its constituent molecules, H_2O. So what is it about this simple structure that gives water its special and exceptional properties, and what are these special properties? The most important to the world we live in are that ice floats on water whereas the solid forms of other liquids sink. Then the heat needed to change water into vapour is greater than with most other liquids; it takes approximately twice as much heat to warm up a given quantity of water as to warm a smilar amount of other substances. Again water conducts electricity, as do solutions in water of many substances (called electrolytes). These are some of the special properties of water – how does its structure explain them?

When teaching about the structure of water molecules, I used to use Lewis Carroll's poem *The Walrus and the Carpenter* as a useful analogy:

After Tenniel

'Oh Oysters come and walk with us along the briny beach.
We cannot do with more than four to give a hand to each.'

The oxygen atoms are like the Walrus (or the Carpenter), each being able to handle two oysters. The hydrogen atoms are like oysters – they only have one hand each. The arms of the Carpenter (and the Walrus) are not horizontal as in the 'arms outstretched' position, but slope down towards the oysters. The H_2O molecule has a similar shape, with the bonds joining the oxygen to the hydrogen forming an angle with each other:

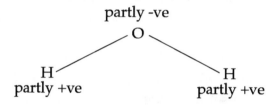

The nuclei of atoms are positively charged and are held together by a negatively charged electron cloud. Because the oxygen atom carries a bigger positive charge than the hydrogen atom it has a major share of the electron cloud that forms the bonds between them. The molecule is therefore called a dipole. (It is as if the head of the Walrus (and of the Carpenter) were negatively charged compared with their feet.) Because they are electrical dipoles, there is a strong force of attraction between the molecules themselves, rather like the attraction between two bar magnets. It takes a lot of energy to separate them and, as we shall see, this is the property of its molecules that makes water different from other liquids in so many ways.

The most outstanding and unique property of water is that ice floats on it. When any other liquid is cooled it gets continuously denser, right down to the freezing point, when the liquid becomes solid. Being denser than the surrounding liquid, the solid sinks to the bottom. I used to demonstrate this to students by cooling some benzene in a test-tube. At the freezing point we observed crystals of solid benzene being formed and falling to the bottom of the tube.

This does not happen with water. As it is cooled, the density of the water increases – but not right down to the freezing points O°C. At 4°C a change occurs and the density begins to *decrease*. So at the freezing point, when the liquid turns to solid, the ice is less dense than the surrounding water and it floats.

This extraordinary unique behaviour of water is, of course, vital to the survival of pond life and, in fact, all aquatic life. Every time I look at my pond in winter I reflect that, if the ice did not float but sank to the bottom, all life in the pond, from goldfish and snails to daphne and amoeba, would perish. As it is, pond life hibernates snugly at the bottom, protected from extreme cold by the layer of ice floating on the top.

> A wizard who wanted to alter
> The normal behaviour of water
> Willed the ice in his moat
> To sink and not float
> Causing vast piscatorial slaughter.

> *G.V.P.*

The strong force of attraction between the molecules of water is also responsible for the other ways in which water is exceptional. One is that it takes more energy to warm up a given mass of water than is the case with other liquids. As with all liquids, the molecules of water are in constant random motion, moving around in all directions – they have 'kinetic energy'. This kinetic energy increases as the temperature of the water is raised, but in the case of water, energy is needed not only to increase the kinetic energy of the molecules but also to counteract the attraction of the dipoles for each other and pull them further apart. So the energy needed to raise the temperature of 1 gram of water is greater than that of other liquids.

This is why more energy is needed to warm up lakes and oceans than to warm the land mass surrounding them. This means that the temperature of the sea or of a lake or inland sea remains more equable than that of the land nearby. This was brought home to me when I was spending a few days in a game lodge in Uganda. It was on the banks of the river a mile or so below the Murchison Falls. Here there were so many hippos that the river seemed to be seething with them. Large numbers of crocodiles lounged around in the warm sand at the side of the river, often taking off into the water and thrashing around with their tails. I was rather amused to read recently that the crocodiles can remain in their rivers until late in the evening, after the tourists have gone back to their lodges, because as night falls the river water stays warmer than the adjacent land.

Another unusual property of water is that the energy needed to boil it is exceptionally high. This again is because the energy needed to pull the dipoles apart from each other and eject them from the liquid into the vapour state is greater than for molecules that are not dipoles. You become conscious of these high energies when you are impatiently waiting for a kettle to boil (and when you get the fuel bill!). When steam condenses, the energy comes out as heat. No doubt you have experienced this when you scalded your hand in the steam from a kettle of boiling water, or when you were in a sauna. A steam scald is worse than one from boiling water because you get a double dose of energy released on to your skin. I have only once had a sauna and that was in a simple steam room in Penang. The room was so full of dense 'steam' that I could not see my way to the exit and began to panic. I've never had another sauna since.

The dipole structure of water is also responsible for another of its important properties – it is an electrolyte. This means that, when it conducts electricity, it is decomposed into its elements, hydrogen and oxygen. The story of how this was first done is quite interesting:

The electric battery had only just been invented. This was done in Italy by Alessandro Volta who made a stack of discs of silver and zinc sheet separated by paper moistened by salt solution. This arrangement became known as the 'Voltaic Pile'. It generated a voltage between its two ends – enough to give an electric shock when touched by the fingers. Volta described his invention in a letter to Sir Joseph Banks, President of the Royal Society, of which Volta was a Fellow. England and France were at war at the time and the letter had to be sent across France. For safety it was sent in two parts – both arrived, but separated by several months.

Two English chemists, William Nicholson and Anthony

Carlisle, were the first to make use of Volta's invention. They constructed their own 'pile' from the description given in Volta's letter and used it to pass an electric current through a sample of water. They found that the current split up the water into the gases hydrogen and oxygen.

Any mention of electricity prior to 1800 referred either to flashes of lightning or to the charge you can get by rubbing your comb on your sleeve and using it to pick up little bits of paper or to make your hair stand on end. When lightning flashes a momentary current flows from cloud to cloud (or cloud to earth) but *continuous* flows of electricity were not possible until Volta invented the electric pile or battery.

Water not only conducts electricity itself, but enables a number of other substances to do so when they are dissolved in water. The use of water as the liquid in all types of electrolytic cell, such as the car battery, is well known. Many chemical industries use the process of electrolysis to purify crude substances, such as copper (see Chapter 13). Electrolysis is also used to turn the electrolyte into a new, different substance, for example molten common salt can be turned into the metal sodium and the poisonous gas, chlorine.

Water and Life

Life may have begun in a muddy pool of water, although steaming vents at deep sea level are now favoured. But however life may have started, water continues to play a vital part in living processes. We ourselves are about 70% water, an elephant is also about 70%, a potato about 80%

and a tomato about 95%. The role of water in living processes is truly remarkable – without the passage of water in and out of the cells, carrying various substances in solution, life could not continue. Blood and lymph can flow around the body, consisting, as they do, largely of water. All living processes – digestion, the passage of foodstuffs around the tissues, excretion of waste – rely on water as a medium of transport. (I have read that after drinking a pint of water, the last drop does not leave our bodies until 13 days later.)

The importance of water is nowhere greater than in countries trying to grow crops in hot, dry climates. We are only too familiar with the horrendous human tragedies that occur when 'the rains fail'; the land dries up, crops cannot be grown; great numbers of people starve and many die. Irrigation has, of course, been used since time immemorial, but original thinking and research is developing methods that make more efficient use of the irrigation water. In Israel a process was developed called 'drip irrigation', in which water is delivered where it is needed by plants, i.e. only a few inches below the surface of the soil. In this way agricultural engineers have enabled 'the desert to flourish'.

> 'Water, water everywhere
> Nor any drop to drink'
>
> (*The Rime of the Ancient Mariner*,
> Samuel Taylor Coleridge)

Obtaining pure water from sea water has long been a problem. To boil the sea water and condense the vapour as water is possible but expensive in energy. In spite of this, distillation processes produce about 75% of all desalinated water at present. Smaller pieces of equipment can be carried by adventurous yachtsmen and others. These mostly use the principle of 'ion exchange', familiar in many households in the form of water softeners. They work by passing the water through granules which include sodium ions in their structures. The ions that make water 'hard', i.e. calcium and magnesium, change places with the sodium ions in the granules, thus leaving the water 'soft'.

When I was in Israel in the late sixties, running a course on the teaching of chemistry in (believe it or not) Jerusalem, I was taken on a trip through the hills till we came down to the level of the Dead Sea. Here we saw the factories set up to get pure water from the sea water. There are others in the Gulf States, in the USA and elsewhere. The principles behind these larger-scale desalination plants are twofold. One makes use of 'reverse osmosis', the other of 'electro-dialysis', the principles of which I will now describe.

'Osmosis' is the process that occurs when water enters a solution through a membrane; 'reverse osmosis' refers to water leaving a solution through a membrane. Technically this is not as simple as it sounds, but nevertheless reverse osmosis can be used to produce pure water from brackish water, and even sea-water.

I used to start to teach osmosis by discussing the experiments of Abbé Nollet in the last part of the 18th century. The first experiments he carried out used a pig's bladder as the membrane. In 1748 Abbé Nollet filled a pig's bladder with alcohol, tied up the neck of the bladder and placed it in water. The bladder swelled up and eventually burst (it can't have been a very pleasant experiment to perform!). Evidently water was entering the bladder faster than alcohol was coming out. The stuff of which the bladder consists was therefore later called a 'semi-permeable membrane' (a misnomer – such membranes are not 'semi-permeable', they are just more permeable to one stuff than to another and are now called 'differential membranes').

Among those who improved semi-permeable membranes was a German scientist named Traube in 1882. To me Traube was just a name in a textbook – the name of a scientist who had invented better semi-permeable membranes – but in 1930, when I was a research student at Cambridge, my supervisor, Professor Eric Rideal, took me to a party held in a marquee in the Astronomical Society's grounds. 'You see that old man over there?', he said. 'That's Traube.' I was amazed – I thought he must long since have departed this life. In 1939 he had to flee from the Nazi regime and worked at the University of Edinburgh until his death in 1943. When Professor Rideal referred to him as an 'elderly man' he was about 70 years old – not so great an age these days!

To design a desalinating plant making use of this principle of reverse osmosis requires the use of membranes capable of withstanding these high pressures. Various forms of plastic sheets are currently in use. A means of maintaining high pressures on the salt water must also be devised. Such plants are at present mostly used for obtaining fresh water from the brackish water of inland seas, where the pressures needed are not so high as in the case of sea water.

A second process for desalinating water makes use of 'electro-dialysis'. This process uses a battery of plastic membranes through which the ions of the salts in the water are forced by the application of a high voltage. By using a batch of cells, the ions are moved out of the water, the positive ions to one end, the negative ions to the other, leaving the water less salt than it was.

There is a great deal more that could be written about the properties of water. It is a good solvent: very many substances dissolve in water – salts, sugars, dyestuffs, fertilisers, pesticides – the list is endless. Furthermore, water reacts chemically with a great number of substances to produce other chemicals.

One of the most spectacular chemical reactions with water, dear to the hearts of all chemistry teachers, involves the metal sodium. How often have we tossed a little bit of sodium (the size of a rice grain for the timid, but as big as a green pea for the bold) on to the surface of water in a bowl. However, if you want to see a really impressive demonstration you must visit (as I did in the late forties) a sodium factory on the shores of a lake in Norway. After seeing the electrolysis plant where the sodium was manufactured in the form of 'bricks', we walked out a few yards on to the quayside and watched while our guide threw a brick of sodium (much the same size as a traditional building brick) into the lake. A tall fountain arose from where the 'brick' landed and reacted with the water to produce hydrogen. Small chunks of sodium were thrown a few feet around it. These too reacted, throwing smaller chunks further out to give more small fountains, and so on ad infinitum – a most spectacular demonstration and a sample of the huge quantities of energy that can be liberated by certain chemical reactions.

Add this to its vital role in the oceans and the skies and in the maintenance of life on earth, and you can see why I have said that water is the most wonderful substance in the world.

Now water has been found in a meteorite brought to earth in March 1988 in Texas, the first time water of extra-terrestrial origin has been identified. Ref: *The Times*, Science Editor, 27 August 1999. It was found inside small crystals of rock salt in the meteorite. The water, instead of dissolving salt in the oceans, had changed roles and was found inside the salt. So we can now say that water is not only the most wonderful stuff in the world, but in the universe!

In contrast to all this serious stuff I cannot resist passing on to my readers the reflections of a 'drinking friend' – 'After drinking a few whiskies and water, I get a terrible headache. It's the same with gin and water, and also with brandy and water. I can only conclude that water is very bad for me.'

CHAPTER 4: OIL

Mineral or vegetable – confuse them at your peril!

'Some words are like a portmanteau and there are two
meanings packed into one word', said Humpty Dumpty
(*Alice Through the Looking Glass*, Lewis Carroll.)

'OIL' IS LIKE THAT: does it make you think of the liquid
you put in the engine of your car? Or the oil you put
in your frying pan? Or perhaps of the soothing ointment
you put on your skin? Or of the medicine you give your
children for their health? The word is defined as 'one of
any number of viscous liquids with a smooth sticky feel'.
(Some oils feel slippery rather than 'sticky'). Here is a list
of examples included in the word 'oil':

Mineral Oils	
Fuels	Petrol, paraffin oil, diesel oil
Lubricants	Penetrating oil
Vegetable Oils	
Cooking oils	Sunflower oil, olive oil, groundnut oil
Medicines	Castor oil
Cosmetics	Rose oil, lavender oil
Sealant	Linseed oil

They are classified as mineral oils or vegetable oils, according to whether they come from petroleum deposits in the earth's crust or from plants. The two groups are different in their properties and uses and provide a good example of the generalisation that the properties and behaviour of a substance depend upon its molecular structure: 'It is what it is and does what it does because it is as it is'.

Mineral Oils

In 1957 I had the opportunity to visit the oil-fields at Kirkuk in the north of Iraq. I was fascinated to see the gas seeping through the ground and catching fire in many places, and was impressed by the great aluminium towers gleaming in the desert sun.

First I had a few days in Baghdad. It was extremely hot, reaching 124°F in the shade. I remember collapsing into a chair in the air-conditioned office of the Iraq Petroleum Company after being stuck in a traffic jam in the city. The company flew me up to Kirkuk in a small plane. A few other passengers were seated when I got into the aeroplane. A burly fellow in shorts then boarded. As he walked towards the pilot's seat, he said: 'They let me fly solo now'. I find flights in small planes sufficiently frightening without that sort of badinage!

It was, of course, also extremely hot in the desert in Kirkuk and as we toured the various installations, we were handed a glass of salt water at frequent intervals. There was not only the heat to contend with but also the all-pervading smell of crude oil. In places the oil seeps out from a rocky outcrop, often catching fire and continuing to burn day and night (*photograph*). At other places natural gas, emerging from patches in the gravelly ground, burns with flickering blue flames over the surface. Tradition says that one of these was the 'burning fiery furnace' into which Nebuchadnezzar cast Shadrach, Meshach and Abed-nego, as recorded in the Book of Daniel in the Old Testament (*photograph*).

Oil was known to exist in Kirkuk for thousands of years, as shown by ancient references to Baba Gurgu, the 'Eternal Fires'. An oil gusher was discovered in 1927 at Baba Gurgu near Kirkuk, after which the oil field was opened up. It was an exceptionally large field and easy to work. The aluminium towers and pipes of the purification plant formed a striking 'island city' in the midst of the yellow sandy desert. After purification, the oil was taken by pipelines to the coast for export (*photograph*). The price of oil at the time I visited Iraq (1957) was 35p a ton at the well-head, £6 a ton by the time it reached the Mediterranean and £70 a ton after being refined. The Iraq Petroleum Development Board planned to spend the oil revenues on developing basic industries in the country. They told me at the time that these would include three dams and hydro-electric power stations, chemical and petro-chemical industries manufacturing fertilizers and plastics, sugar from beet and dates, steel from iron ore found in the north of the country and paper from the rushes grown in the swampy areas. The Iran-Iraq war played havoc with all these plans.

The petroleum found in the oil fields in many parts of the world occurs at varying depths and in a number of geological strata, but the deposits are all millions of years old. The stuff varies in its composition – most is liquid but some is gaseous. Mineral oils are extracted from natural oil or petroleum by splitting it up into fractions of different boiling points, the most volatile mineral oil being petrol. The molecules of mineral oils consist mainly of long chains of carbon atoms, to which are joined slightly more than twice as many hydrogen atoms, like this:

$$CH_3 - CH_2 - CH_2 - - - CH_2 - CH_3$$

They are known as paraffins ('of little affinity'), as they are not very reactive chemicals. Their chemical name is alkanes. The chains vary greatly in length – from 4 to over 25 carbon atoms – and may include double bonds between the carbon atoms (see *Glossary*). There is therefore a great variety of petroleum compounds, ranging from natural gas, whose molecules are relatively small, containing only up to 4 or 5 carbon atoms, through petrol and paraffin to diesel oil, with molecules with higher numbers of atoms in each. Here is a list of substances obtained from crude oil. They are separated from each other by a process called 'fractional distillation', in which the oil is first heated to vaporise it and then the vapours are condensed back at a series of temperatures to produce the various liquid fractions. This is what is going on in the shiny metal towers you see in an oil refinery.

It is interesting to note that the greater the number of carbon atoms in the molecule, the higher the boiling point of the oil.

Petroleum Product	Boiling point o°C	No of carbon atoms per molecule	Examples of Uses
Natural Gas	Under 40°	less than 4	Heating
Gasoline	40°–160°	4–10	Car engines. Petro-chemicals
Kerosene	160°–250°	10–16	Paraffin stoves. Jet engines
Light gas oil	250°–300°	16–20	For splitting up, 'cat cracking', to produce petrol
Heavy gas oil	300°–350°	20–25	Diesel engines
Residues	Over 350°	over 25	Wax, bitumen

Although petroleum oils are mixtures obtained from mineral sources, descriptions of their chemistry are found in textbooks about organic chemistry. This is, of course, because their origin was living plants, probably single-cell plankton living in a marine environment up to 550 million years ago. These were buried during later geological eras and were mineralised by heat and pressure deep in the earth's crust to become petroleum. The energy tied up in fossil fuels originated from solar energy 'fixed' many millions of years ago through photosynthesis.

At first the distinction between 'organic' and 'inorganic' chemicals was clear – organic chemicals were those produced from living organisms and inorganic were derived from mineral sources. It was thought that some kind of 'vital force' present in living organisms was influential in the formation of organic chemical compounds. Then, in 1828, a chemist working in Göttingen in the Harz Mountains in Germany, Friedrich Wöhler, made an undoubtedly organic compound, urea, by gently heating an inorganic salt, ammonium cyanate, and the distinction between organic and inorganic compounds disappeared. We are familiar with urea as a constituent of urine – there is no doubt whatever that it is an animal product. Although we may think that some 'vital force' goes into its production, there is no 'vital force' concerned with ammonium cyanate (although the controversy was not finally settled until 1845). Friedrich Wöhler thus played an important part in the history of chemistry. Unknown to him, he also influenced the career of my friend Willy Turner. He owes his very successful career to Friedrich Wöhler.

Willy started life as a clerk in the Civil Service and rose to a high position in the Chamber of Commerce. As a young man he was determined to get to a university and he studied hard during his spare time to pass the entrance examination to Imperial College, London. He had studied the sciences at school and all three were subjects in the examination. Unfortunately he was not good at chemistry. So he concentrated on Physics and Biology. He still had to pass in a subsidiary chemistry paper. He had difficulty in remembering the formulae and equations that seemed to be an essential part of chemistry. So he scoured previous chemistry papers looking for a question that cropped up often and for which he would be able to 'mug up' the answer. His choice fell on Friedrich Wöhler's synthesis of urea. He was lucky – the question appeared. He must have answered it well for he passed the exam, went to university and never looked back. He remained so grateful to Wöhler that later in life, when on holiday in Germany, he always visited Göttingen University and paid homage to the statue and memorial plaque erected in Wöhler's memory.

Another young man in a similar situation was not so lucky – you may know this story, but, unlike that of Willy Turner, I think it is just a story! This chap was taking an examination in Physics, about which he knew very little. However, he did know how a pump worked and prayed that there would be a question about a pump. When he opened the question paper, alas there was no question on pumps. So he had to choose another question. His answer began: 'Before it is possible to answer this question, it is necessary to describe the principle of the common pump'. Of course, he failed.

Benzene and Michael Faraday

I once took a party of sixth-formers to visit the Royal Institution in London. Its most famous Director was Michael Faraday, a successor to Sir Humphry Davy, the discoverer of sodium and other elements. Faraday became interested in chemistry when, as apprentice to a bookbinder, he was binding a book called *Conversations in Chemistry* by Mrs Jane Marcet. I have a copy of this fascinating book, in which Mrs Marcet has socratic conversations with two girl pupils, Emily and Caroline. Emily was a model pupil, absorbing all she was told, but Caroline was a bit 'difficult' and made awkward remarks like 'Yes, I am very familiar with the earth Magnesia – it is a medicine'. Faraday wrote that it was 'in books, in the hours after work, I found the beginning of my philosophy. There were two that especially helped me, the *Encyclopaedia Britannica* and Mrs Marcet's *Conversations in Chemistry* ... When I questioned her book, by such little experiments as I could find means to perform, and found them true to the facts as described by Mrs Marcet, I felt that I had got hold of an anchor in chemical knowledge and clung to it. You may imagine my delight when I came to know Mrs Marcet personally.'

It was of course a privilege for our party to be taken to the basement of the Royal Institution by the then the Director, Professor Andrade, and to see the laboratory where Faraday had worked. Some things that I had not known before stick in my memory – the samples of special glass and of stainless steel – substances with which the name of Faraday is not normally associated. Most impressive was the little phial of a murky liquid – benzene – that Faraday had obtained by distilling crude petroleum.

Benzene is a hydrocarbon with a very different structure from the paraffins. In 1825 Faraday distilled crude oil and found that one of the first liquids to distil over was a colourless liquid of unusual smell, boiling at only 80°C. It was a hydrocarbon but turned out to contain an unusually high percentage of carbon and to have the molecular formula C_6H_6. When you try to write a structure of its molecule, you find that it does not fit in with the generality of other hydrocarbons. Its structure was a puzzle. The solution of the puzzle by Kekulé of Germany is one of the most famous examples in the history of science. It is said that Kekulé was riding on a tram thinking about molecules consisting of chains of carbon atoms. They were wriggling about like serpents. Then, as he watched them in his imagination, one of the serpents got hold of its tail in its mouth. The carbon chain became a ring – and the idea of a ring structure of benzene was born (see *Glossary*).

Benzene has been a useful solvent for over a century and is a chemical used in the preparation of many other compounds like aniline dyes and explosives, but during the past 30 years its production has increased seven-fold. The reason is that over 50% is used in the manufacture of styrene for making polystyrene. The traditional uses amount to only 6%. The main source of benzene is still petroleum: 60% comes from the 'cat crackers' (short for 'catalytic crackers') in which the bigger molecules of the 'light gas oil', boiling at 250 – 300°, are broken down to smaller molecules used for petrol. 'High octane' petrol used to contain benzene, but no longer, because it is bad for the environment, being carcinogenic.

In 1990 the USA introduced cleaner additives than benzene to their gasoline. These were compounds containing oxygen and they enabled the fuel to burn more cleanly. This reduced the exhaust emissions of carbon monoxide and hydrocarbons and also reduced the combustion chamber deposits. Some ethers have been used as additives. In Brazil, and some other countries, 10% of ethanol has been added to petrol for many years. It has the additional advantage of being produced from growing crops such as grain rather than from mineral oil, which presumably will run out one day. (When I was at school in the mid-twenties we were told that supplies of petroleum would all be used up by 1934.) The American National Laboratory claims that if ethanol were to replace conventional gasoline, its use could reduce the energy used from fossil fuel (petroleum) by up to 60%

and the emission of greenhouse gases (carbon dioxide) by up to 45%.

Because it can be carcinogenic, the use of benzene in school laboratories has been banned for about 30 years, together with its related compounds nitrobenzene and aniline. These were commonly used in the study of organic chemistry – I used them all for over 30 years – I even used benzene for cleaning dirty flasks and other apparatus that had become stained by use in organic chemical reactions. However, I survived.

Vegetable Oils

We are most familiar with vegetable oils (i.e. those from vegetable rather than mineral sources) in connection with cooking. I have often wondered whether a light mineral oil such as paraffin would be suitable for use in the frying pan, but I am pretty sure that the flavour imparted to the food would not be acceptable! I have heard of a mountaineer who used vaseline to fry bacon – the result was horrible.

> There was an old cook up at Filey
> Who valued old candle-ends highly
> When no-one was looking
> He used them for cooking
> 'It's wicked to waste', he said dryly.
>
> G.V.P.

Cooking oils come in a variety of forms but all are made from the fruits or seeds of plants such as coconuts, olives, sunflowers and ground nuts. The oils are first refined to reduce the colour and remove odours. Margarine, and other butter substitutes, are emulsified vegetable oils.

I once visited a palm oil mill in Malaysia, where I saw two different oils being extracted from the palm nuts : one is extracted from the kernels of the nuts and the other from the rest of the nut. Each oil is different, and they are marketed separately (see *Glossary*). The nuts grow in clusters on the palm trees (*photograph*). The older trees are quite tall (up to 20 ft) and it is hard work cutting off the bunches of nuts. Latterly this task has been made easier by growing trees less than 6 ft high, where the branches of nuts are more accessible. After cutting them off, the nuts are pounded and 'cooked' in autoclaves with water. They are then subjected to a process called steam distillation in which steam is blown through the seed-mass. When the steam emerges from the still, it carries the vegetable oil with it. These oils float on water so it is not difficult to separate them from the condensed steam. However, some oils have a small solubility in water, so further processing is needed.

Natural oils, useful for other purposes than cooking, are also obtained from many other plants. A friend of mine used to grow roses in Kenya and export them to Japan, but he found it more profitable (but much harder technically) to extract the rose oil and export that. His father, an ingenious engineer, designed a suitable still for him and had it built in Rochester, Kent and exported to Africa. It was then used not only for making rose oil, but also for extracting the natural oils from a number of other crops such as lemon grass.

The molecules of vegetable oils are more complex than

those of mineral oils. They consist of one molecule of glycerine combined with three molecules of a fatty acid. For example, in palm oil the glycerine is combined with palmitic acid, and in olive oil with oleic acid (see *Glossary*). In the industry, natural oils and fats are classified as vegetable (such as palm, coconut, soya bean), animal (such as tallow from beef or mutton and lard from pork) and marine (such as whale or herring). All these are tri-glycerides – quite unlike petroleum oils in their structures (see *Glossary*).

It may interest you to know that human fat contains 47% of oleic acid and 24% of palmitic acid, the rest consisting of two other organic acids, linoleic (10%) and stearic (8%). The latter is found in mutton fat and, as a high percentage, in candle wax, although nowadays this is largely made from paraffin wax.

So oils are another group of substances from which chemists and chemical engineers have produced – and continue to produce – many products that are of use in our everyday life.

The Busy Bee

As a bee I am famous for toil
From pollen I make Jelly Royal
One thing I can't do
And must leave it to you
Is to split up petroleum oil.

G.V.P.

CHAPTER 5: GREASE

A war-time thriller

NEAR THE START OF WORLD WAR II a German and a British destroyer came within firing range of each other but, because they were so heavily iced up, neither ship could fire a shot. On another occasion a British merchant ship had accumulated so much ice on her superstructure that she turned over. Why did such things happen? To supply our Russian allies, ships sailed from the Shetland Islands to the port of Murmansk in Northern Russia. The route is normally ice-free throughout the year owing to the warm waters of the Gulf Stream but, because of danger from enemy air attack from aircraft based in Norway, British convoys to Russia were forced to leave the Gulf Stream and take more northerly routes, where, under certain weather conditions, accumulation of ice on the ships became a serious menace. In these colder and more stormy regions of the Arctic bitter winds from the north are often encountered. The superstructure of ships may therefore get extremely cold and any spray blown over it freezes immediately. When this occurs, ice may build up at rates exceeding one inch an hour to form a layer three inches thick or more. The weather causing maximum icing will be wet and windy, so that the difficulties for the crew in trying to remove the ice from the ship's mechanisms on deck will be great, the motion of the ship adding its own hazards to those due to the extreme cold. In peacetime the winches and other iced-up machinery could be freed by steam or hot water jets. This is not practical in heavy seas. Anyway, the liquid water soon freezes up again, causing problems on the decks and walkways.

At this time I was working for the Ministry of Supply under a Dr A.S.C. Lawrence, who had been a colleague of mine when I was a research student at Cambridge. Lawrence was an expert on surface chemistry and could make the biggest soap bubbles I have ever seen. We were a small group of three and, together with our laboratory assistant, we worked at Imperial College, South Kensington. When we were given the problem of the de-icing of ships to solve we decided to visit a ship in Portsmouth Dockyard that had just returned from the Arctic. My diary records that 'On October 8th 1943 we left London for Portsmouth. It was a glorious autumn day. The sun shone, though a little misty at first, on the lovely autumn tints, lighting up the southern slopes of the South Downs. The police on the Dockyard gates directed us to the officers' mess. After an excellent lunch we inspected a destroyer that had seen much Arctic service, and another in good condition. It was made clear to us by the officers that any attempts to prevent the formation of ice (such as fitting steam pipes below deck) were futile. On the other hand anything that could be done to make the ice easier to remove would be 'well worthwhile.' Ice adheres to the surface of clean metal or paint with great tenacity;

the force required to shear it off may be up to one ton per square foot. A thin film of a suitable oil reduces this by at least 90 per cent. However, any kind of de-icing oil or grease applied to the ship's surfaces must also be able to withstand heavy weathering at moderate temperatures for several days while the ship is on its way to the Arctic.

These requirements needed some stuff with rather special properties: it must adhere to the ship's surface without being washed off by heavy storms at moderate temperatures, but it must also remain pliable below freezing temperatures so that the ice can be removed. To develop such substances we designed and made two pieces of test apparatus. One was a gale tunnel in which we could fire drops of water at a speed of 120 mph at a grease-covered steel plate to see if the grease remained in place. The other was a device for measuring the force needed to slide a block of ice off the greasy plate at temperatures down to −30°C. After a few weeks' work, we produced two materials that came up to specification. One was an oil for spraying on flat surfaces; the other was a putty-like stuff for wrapping round coarse mechanisms to prevent the ice keying-in and locking them. It consisted of a grease containing asbestos fibres to stiffen it.

Two months after starting the work, the experimental results had progressed enough for us to hold a conference involving naval officers and representatives of the industries that were to produce the de-icing materials. I shall never forget the expressions of horror on the faces of the naval officers when we suggested spraying the superstructure of their ships with greasy oil. Four weeks later the material had been manufactured by the hundredweight and was ready for ships' trials.

Here are some extracts from my diary which I hope will give a flavour of what it was like to be involved in such research:

'September 13th 1943: worked on the wind tunnel now functioning out on the roof. Improved the spray which, with the wind, had a mud-pie effect on a medium grease being tested on the plates. Saturday 18th: removed the wind tunnel to the ground floor where water could be laid on. Waiting for the electrician to finish the job. 20th September: motor now wired up and working, giving a powerfully blown spray, probably about 60 mph. Various tests were tried out – general purpose grease (GS) and a Shell asbestos compound were the only ones that really stood up to the test. The latter was analysed and some stuff made up with asbestos extracted from it. Pulley blocks were packed with it and frozen in a bucket of water in the fridge. They came out looking like prawns in aspic and gave a good impression of the whole problem.

'September 28th: the much-postponed conference at the Ministry of Supply on de-icing was attended by twenty-four persons, including naval officers and representatives of various Admiralty Departments. Impressive photographs of ice-bound ships were shown, giving a useful picture of the conditions we had to work with. October 1st: made up pastes with new asbestos samples in the GS grease. 14th October: drew up lists of parts of a ship that were suitable for de-icing paste. Tried a number of new pastes, none so good as the GS grease/asbestos mixture, now known as No 35. Prepared a large quantity of this using Miss Slinfield's mincing machine. (Miss Slinfield was our very loyal laboratory assistant.) October 18th: visited a rope factory on the Isle of Dogs to see how rope was made. A very interesting factory. To prevent rope icing up or to thaw it when it has iced up is going to be a very difficult problem.

'27th October: bought a new piece of apparatus to measure the speed in the wind tunnel. The result was that it turned out to be much faster than we had thought, 130 mph instead of 60. 1st November: did some cooling experiments to find out where the various stuffs harden up. Shell asbestos compound, softened with oleic acid and creosol, weathered quite well; in fact it stayed in the gale tunnel for our longest test, nearly 65 minutes. Started a new ice pulling-off apparatus. 8th November: prepared notes for meeting with grease-makers tomorrow. At the meeting the grease-makers made various helpful suggestions, and will submit samples to us for test in a week's time.

'November 15th: Went to Leeds with Lawrence to see grease made. Very dirty and slippery factories. Saw stores of oil of various kinds. After an excellent lunch, went to see more grease made by distillation. Foul smell. Caught the 5.30 train back. 3 hours late, so spent the night in Kings Cross Hotel in a bad temper.

'Monday 22nd November: Lawrence away with flu.

'25th November: Miss Slinfield also away – going to get married on Saturday. Prepared new pull-off experiments with simple brass troughs. Lawrence turned up about tea-time, surly and coughing. We decided to get large batches made.

'December 1st: More samples arrived. Arranged for cold chamber tests tomorrow. Admiralty have suddenly decided on ship trials in 9 days time.

'December 2nd: Visited the cold chambers of the El Dorado ice cream company. Took three large iron sheets and a barrel of grease with us. Cold chamber contained many trays of fruit: strawberries, raspberries, gooseberries etc. Returned the following day and hacked off the ice from the iron sheets with my geological hammer. Fresh samples from Shell works were disappointing. Discussed further batches to be made up over the weekend.

'December 5th: Sudden developments – sea trials are to start earlier – it was to have been Sunday, now tomorrow, Thursday. All rushing round buying ice-picks etc.

'December 6th: Lawrence left with a suit case, no shirts, a large packet of Epsom salts, some films and the ice-picks. Next day we sent the shirts off by plane.'

Lawrence was to join *Wrestler*, an old 'W' class destroyer. This was one of the ships escorting a convoy to Murmansk involved in a plan to lure the German battleship *Scharnhorst* into the hands of the British FLEET. The battleship *Duke of York* was to sail from Iceland and sink the *Scharnhorst*, thus rescuing the convoy and its escorts. Should the battleship not arrive in time, *Wrestler* was to close in on the *Scharnhorst*, fire its two torpedoes and retreat at full speed. Fortunately all went according to plan and the *Scharnhorst* was sunk, but Lawrence had some nervous days waiting! During that time, and in very heavy weather, he applied the de-icing material to appropriate parts of the ship and they stood up well to the stormy rain. Unfortunately no icing conditions were encountered, so the effectiveness of the materials as de-icing agents could not be assessed on that occasion.

Many years later a totally different principle was tried out on Canadian vessels visiting Arctic waters. A solution of a lacquer was painted on surfaces where ice was expected to form. After a certain thickness of ice had built up, a sharp blow fractured the brittle layer of lacquer and the ice fell off. That was the theory – but I don't know if it worked in practice.

CHAPTER 6: FOOD

Growing it, cooking it and eating it

A S THE POPULATION OF THE WORLD INCREASES, mankind endeavours to grow more food. This is where chemicals come into the story. Just as we need food, so crops need nourishment. If nothing is added to the soil, the annual crop will get weaker and weaker and eventually will not grow at all. From the earliest days, men seem to have realised this and by means either of leaving fields fallow, crop rotation, threshing and burning, or adding natural fertilizers, they improved the fertility of the soil. Even if nothing is added, bacteria in the soil can capture nitrogen from the air and turn it into a fertiliser.

A colleague of mine, who taught biology, had an impressive poster on the wall of his laboratory showing a painting of a large cow eating a cabbage. At its head was a label: 'Cabbage becoming cow', and at its other end, where dung was being excreted into the soil, a label reading 'Cow becoming cabbage'. It certainly caught the attention of his pupils! From the chemical point of view, these processes enable the 'nitrogen cycle' to be carried out. The air consists of about 4/5th nitrogen: nitrogen is a vital element in living things being an essential part of protein molecules. But getting the nitrogen from the air and into the protein is not so easy. Atmospheric nitrogen can be 'fixed', i.e. turned into chemical compounds, in a number of ways, e.g. lightning causes nitrogen to combine with oxygen in the air and turns it into compounds that are washed into the soil by rain. This process is copied by industries making nitrates. The atmospheric nitrogen can also be 'fixed' by certain clever bacteria, as referred to above. The cow assists the nitrogen cycle by utilising crops for food and depositing nitrogen-containing waste back into the soil. All farmers and gardeners know the meaning of the message the poster was intended to convey – add manure and compost to the soil. Some people believe that this is all that is needed and this may be so in a garden or even a farm. However, it is different in the USA, where immense acreages are cultivated. There it is necessary to supply the growing crops with more nourishment than is normally available from compost and manure.

In 1898 the celebrated British scientist, Sir William Crookes, said: 'All civilised nations stand in deadly peril of not having enough to eat ... It is the chemist who must come to the rescue.' Earlier that century the supply of nitrogen compounds for agriculture (in addition to that produced by thunderstorms and nitrifying bacteria) depended on 'Chile nitrate' (a naturally occurring salt), on guano, and on ammonium sulphate (a by-product from the gasworks). These would never have sufficed for the demands of the 20th century, but processes have been developed which use the nitrogen of the air and cause it to combine with hydrogen (made from water) to make ammonia, which is the basic chemical from which fertilisers are made. These are referred to as 'artifical fertilisers', but they consist of the same chemicals (nitrogen compounds) as are supplied to crops by nature.

Two friends and I were once on holiday in Norway and visited the Rjukan valley, where these chemical processes were being carried out. We saw the great dam built at the head of the valley to hold water for use at the hydro-electric plant there. (The plant was the objective of one of the most famous raids by British forces during the War, of which a film was made: *The Heroes of Telemark*. The reason why the plant was an important target was that the electricity produced there was used, among other things, for making 'heavy water', a substance used in the construction of atomic bombs.) The electricity from the huge generators was used to electrolyse water which was split into the gases hydrogen and oxygen. These were needed as raw materials for the chemical industries, a kilometre or so below in the valley. The sides of the valley were very steep and for several weeks in the year no sun reached the valley bottom. For the sake of those who lived there, lifts were provided so that people could travel up into the sun.

The complex of industries at the foot of the valley included the Birkeland-Eyde process and the Haber-Bosch process. Both manufactured chemicals used for agricultural purposes. The former used oxygen, combining it with nitrogen from the air to make nitrogen oxides for conversion to nitrates. The Haber process used hydrogen and nitrogen to manufacture ammonia. So both the hydrogen and the oxygen gases generated at the hydro-electric plant had to be separately conveyed for about a kilometre down the valley to the industrial area. This was done by the use of large aluminium pipes borne by aluminium supports firmly concreted into the ground and including expansion joints at intervals to prevent buckling in the heat. What surprised us was there were *three* pipes – not two – one for the hydrogen and one for the oxygen, but what was the third pipe for? Then we thought of water, H_2O, and realised that two pipes were used for the hydrogen and one for the oxygen, a more economical way of dealing with the situation than making two pipes and accessories of different sizes.

Hydrogen is becoming an important fuel but generating it by electrolysis of water, using high voltages, is an expensive process. However, recent research has shown that the cost can be reduced by first exposing the water to sunlight in the presence of an iron catalyst. This can be done in open pools where the sunlit water accumulates energy that renders it capable of being split into hydrogen and oxygen, using lower voltages, making the process less expensive. (*Chemistry and Industry*, 16.8.99, p.620)

It seems that the food problem is going to be with us for many years to come. Kenneth Woodridge in *Chemistry and Industry* (May 1998) wrote that: 'Human activities have now overtaken nature as the main source of fixed nitrogen and this trend is accelerating. Well over half of the present human contribution to fixed nitrogen is related to the need to produce more food. If the world and GNP continue to grow, fertiliser demand will grow too and may reach saturation by the middle of the next century. However, fertiliser supply does not ensure food adequacy if the area of arable land remains constant. The prospects of increasing the arable land are bleak without dire consequences for the environment.' An Australian friend tells me that when they used to drive from their country home, some thirty miles from the city, it was through arable land that they referred to as the 'bread basket of Melbourne'. Now it consists of built-up suburbs with thousands of new houses. But there is no need to go to Australia for examples. My own garden in Sussex used to border on a farm; this is now covered by a housing estate of more than 3,400 houses.

Controversies continue. According to the popular biologist, Dr David Bellamy, failure to solve the problem of feeding the world will be the cause of the eventual disappearance of the human race from the earth. Scientists try hard – first it was 'artificial fertilisers', the production and use of nitrogen compounds to help nature to supply the soil with enough nitrogen to give bigger crops so as to feed growing populations. The chemists were then accused of polluting the soil and poisoning the rivers. There is a campaign for 'organically grown' food – more expensive but 'free from chemicals'. (I hope the readers know by now how to answer that one: they should ask 'What is a chemical?') Chemists then tried to tackle the loss of foodstuffs through predators – by poisoning harmful insects, bacteria, fungi etc. They were then accused of also poisoning the human consumer.

So the poor beleaguered scientists tried another tack – modify the crops so that the insects don't like them, and leave them for us: 'genetic modification'. I am only a chemist – not a biologist, biochemist, physiologist, or pathologist – but I must admit that I cannot see how switching the position of a few groups on the DNA spiral of rape seed can affect what happens to it in our digestive systems, when it is entirely broken down to carbon dioxide and water. No doubt this is a naive view and the controversy over genetically modified food will continue on its multi-million dollar course for some time yet.

Food Preservation

When I was a boy, I used to put dozens of eggs into a zinc bucket and fill it up with a solution of 'waterglass' (sodium silicate) to preserve the eggs. A lot has changed since then. Nowadays much of the food we buy contains approved preservatives and everything is stamped with its 'sell by' date.

After food is mass-produced in industry, it is often deep-frozen. A low temperature is the best way of preserving food en masse. Salt has been used for centuries for preserving meat. In South East Asia, and no doubt elsewhere, a variety of spices is also used as preservatives. My students in the University in Penang carried out an experiment in the laboratory (which I have recently repeated in my kitchen) to compare the efficacy of several spices. We put small equal pieces of raw meat in separate test tubes to which had been added water and one of the spices. The test was to see how many days it took each to stink (the experiment is best not conducted in a domestic room!). I forget the order found by the students, but the following was the order of efficacy of the spices I used:

Spice	No of days to 'stinking'
Pepper	3
Cumin	3

Spice	No of days to 'stinking'
Chilli	4
Cardamon	6
Mustard	6
Tamarind	10

Cooking It

Do we realise that, as we watch our favourite television cook, we are watching chemical reactions going on? Cooking brings about chemical changes that make the foodstuffs more digestible and, usually, tastier to eat. Most chemical changes that occur in cooking are quite complex but a few will be described below.

When you yourself cook, you are carrying out chemical changes – even when you boil an egg, steam cabbage or grill bacon, you are involving the constituents in them in chemical changes. Baking bread, making cakes, brewing beer or making wine, all involve chemical processes. In my youth Philip Harden was a popular television chef. In his book, *The Grammar of Cooking*, he does not entirely shun mention of chemistry. He picturesquely says: 'The food which the egg stores for the bird-to-be is mainly protein, whereas the grain of wheat providing for the plant-to-be consists of a small amount of protein (called gluten) and a large amount of starch'.

He explains that 'when the flour is subjected to a dry heat it develops a gold-brown crust – this is due to the dextrinisation of starch and other processes, but this book is not the place for the highly complex chemistry of sugar, starch and other carbohydrates – ignorance of the molecular structure of the polysaccharides will not spoil the flavour of your cooking!'

So I must remember that! However, there is one simple bit of chemistry I would like to mention: when you bake bread, cakes, scones etc., something in the dough causes it to 'rise'. This is the carbon dioxide gas given off by the yeast as it grows, or by the baking powder (if you use it) or the self-raising flour (which contains baking powder and saves you putting it in). Baking powder consists of sodium hydrogen carbonate plus an acid such as tartaric acid. This combination, when damp, gives off carbon dioxide, the little bubbles of which, generated within the dough, expand it and lighten it. The carbon dioxide from the yeast has the same effect on the dough, provided the temperature is less than 32°C, above which the yeast dies. In contrast, the lightening effect of the baking powder is speeded up by a little warming.

Here is a different use of chemicals in the kitchen: when you are making a fruit salad and you leave the sliced apple and banana lying around, they begin to turn brown on the surface. They do not do this by magic – it is a chemical change. The oxidising action of the air on the fruit, catalysed by an enzyme, produces a dark pigment called melanin. However, as you may know, the browning effect can be prevented by squeezing lemon juice over the fruit. The lemon juice contains citric acid which inactivates the enzyme and so prevents the air from oxidising the fruit. Incidentally, vitamin C (ascorbic acid) has the same effect, so if you haven't got a lemon, dissolve a little vitamin C in water and sprinkle it over the fruit – I've tried it and it works well.

Do you know the difference between an omelette and a scrambled egg? Many people don't, but 'old Hughes', my one-time colleague in the Department of Colloid Science at Cambridge University – he knew: 'They are both colloids – mixtures of a fatty phase and a watery phase. In the omelette the aqueous part is dispersed in the fat, but in the scrambled egg it is the other way round – the fat is dispersed in the watery phase.' As a cook-chemist you will know that to produce an omelette you must have the fat very hot – smoking in the pan, but for a scrambled egg you must not let the egg mixture get hotter than the boiling point of water or the structure will break down and the egg will be dry and horrid!

Meat

I find meat difficult to cook so that it is always tender. A good fillet of steak is easy – throw it in a very hot oiled pan, turn it over and seal the juices in, then turn the heat down and cook it for a few minutes according to whether you like it rare or well done. A head chef friend of mine makes this decision by poking the steak with his finger!

Some meat (for example stewing steak) requires longer cooking at lower temperatures, e.g. in a casserole. Why is this? Think of meat as consisting of connective tissue and protein. In raw meat the protein (myosin) is a bright red colour, but heat causes the structure to change and the colour to change to brown. This process starts at about 40°C. At about 70°C the molecules of proteins get shorter and the meat tougher, but around 80°C the structure of the proteins breaks down altogether and the meat gets tenderer. So to get the meat cooked nicely, the temperature of the casserole should be about 80°C, too hot to touch but not boiling. It may need an hour or two to tenderise tough meat, so don't put the vegetables into the casserole until the last half hour of cooking or they will finish up as a mush.

The connective tissue (collagen) behaves differently. Between 50°C and 70°C it begins to shrink; further heating and it breaks down to a gelatine-like consistency. So meat with a lot of connective tissue should be cooked in a water-based gravy at about 80°C for a long time, which is also about right for the rest of the proteins.

This is becoming a cookery book, which it is not meant to be! There are plenty already – all beautifully illustrated in colour, but they tell you nothing about the chemical reactions that are taking place. If you want to know about these, you will have to consult books on 'Food Science'.

Eating It

My father used to say: 'A little of what you fancy does you good'. I have found this a practical and effective guide to what I eat. Later in life, I realised that the most important word there is 'little'. As my mother quoted: 'As men and women to forty come, men grow to belly and women to bum'. (Of course, at that time, the last word was not pronounced – we suggested it by the rhyme!).

Like all other 'stuffs', foodstuffs are made of chemicals – carbohydrates, proteins, fats etc. We ourselves consist of 60 – 70% of water. The remaining mass varies a lot from person to person (some are fat, some thin, some muscular etc). Proteins probably make up about 20%, minerals (largely in the bones) account for maybe 10% and the rest will be carbohydrates, DNA etc. Some joker once wrote that:

> The human body contains
> enough fat for 7 bars of soap,
> enough iron for a medium sized nail,
> enough sugar for 7 cups of tea,
> enough lime to whiten 1 chicken run,
> enough phosphorus to tip 200 matches,
> enough magnesium for 1 dose of salts,
> enough potash to explode a toy car, and
> enough sulphur to rid 1 dog of fleas.

These chemicals not only provide nourishment but also energy to keep us going. They say that 'you can climb Mount Everest on a bar of chocolate'. Certainly chocolate is one of the most nutritious foodstuffs and contains the essential constituents: protein, fat and carbohydrates. Ten grams of chocolate provides the consumer with about 230 kilojoules of energy when digested (and 15 g of cheddar cheese yields almost as much). Of course, not all 'chocolate' is the same – the various types differ in their cocoa-bean, sugar and milk content. When using chocolate for cooking, Delia Smith says you should make sure it contains 75% of cocoa.

So when the mouse that took up residence in my study showed a huge appetite for both cheese and chocolate, it was on to a good thing! I will spare the reader details of my preliminary skirmishes with it. Things got serious when I missed a 100-gram slab of chocolate from a shelf in my study. Closer inspection showed that it had fallen on the floor, but when I went to pick it up, I discovered that only the metal foil and coloured paper packaging were there – all the chocolate had gone, leaving the wrapping intact. Furthermore, when I opened a drawer in my desk, little pieces of chocolate, about 1 – 2 cm across, had been stored there. It was a clever mouse, but in the end my humane trap was too cunning for it!

Chocolate is a quick source of energy – 100 g of chocolate contains about 8 g of protein, 35 g of fat and 50 g of carbohydrate. If I feel hungry during the daytime, I nibble a piece of cheese: if I feel hungry during the night I take a chocolate biscuit from the tin beside my bed, or drink a small whisky. Both remedies send me to sleep within minutes. Unfortunate walkers in the snow who fell victim to the cold used to be revived by the brandy brought to them by the St Bernard dog. Modern nutritionists do not think this is a good idea, as the warm feeling soon goes and undesirable side-effects are caused.

The table below shows the average energy available from 100 g of some foodstuffs. (To convert the quantities to calories, divide by 240. For example, the value for chocolate is about 10 calories per 100 grams.)

	Kilojoules per 100g.
Chocolate	2,300
Cheese	1,700
Egg yolk	630
Meat	1,000
Fish	350
Potato	340

	Kilojoules per 100g.
Bread	950
Sugar	1,600

Men need about 12,000 kj per day on average and at least 6,000 to survive; women generally need a little less.

I believe that foodstuffs can be arranged in an order showing the rate at which they provide the body with energy. Alcohol heads the list. Cheese and chocolate soon provide the tired walker with energy and he gets his 'second wind'. Bread probably comes next in the sequence and proteins last. My list is based on the size of the molecules and the ease with which their breakdown products pass through the digestive system into the bloodstream. To do this, they are first broken down by the action of enzymes. Enzymes are defined as 'a group of proteins produced in living cells that catalyse specific biochemical reactions', i.e. they help them to take place more quickly and easily. For example, the enzyme trypsin breaks down proteins to give amino-acids, amylase breaks down starch to sugar and lipase attacks fats to give glycerine and fatty acids (see *Glossary*).

We all know that digestion begins in the mouth where the enzyme ptyalin gets to work. Was it Gladstone who said that soldiers should chew each mouthful 32 times, thus making the maximum use of their rations?

My friend Paul McKeown gives his approval to my including the limerick I wrote about him:

> I have a big friend called McKeown
> Who said to his wife 'What yer doin'?

> You're preparing to make
> A luscious rich cake
> When it's slimming that I am pursuin'.
>
> G.V.P.

To slim, one has to deprive the body of sources of energy so that it burns up some of its own fat. To encourage it to do this it must be deprived of the more accessible sources of energy such as alcohol and sugar. So consuming less alcohol, sugar and other easily digested foodstuffs and, of course, having no fat, should aid slimming. Eating more protein will help with 'body building'.

So, to summarise: for a quick replacement of your energy, take a glass of glucose solution, to build up your strength, eat bread, fish, meat and beans, and to slim leave out alcohol and sugar from your diet, reduce the carbohydrates and eat no fat. (Excess carbohydrate gets converted to fat – so go steady on the rice and potatoes!)

See formulae in *Glossary* for some technical information. You need not study the details of these formulae – just notice that some molecules are bigger than others and that they are built up of only 3 elements: carbon, hydrogen and oxygen, except for the proteins, which also include nitrogen.

As well as providing energy, foods are needed for body building. Proteins are the most important. Also we mustn't forget vitamins. Plenty of fruit and vegetables supply these but many people supplement them with vitamin tablets. Salad vegetables have recently been shown also to keep bones healthy and are better than milk in providing calcium to prevent osteoporosis.

The chemical contents of foodstuffs are always important, but to certain people individual chemicals can be especially significant, as the following story will show (it is adapted from an article by Dr James Le Fanu in *The Sunday Telegraph*, 27.7.98):

> About a year ago I described the sufferings of a Kentish man who for the best part of ten years had chronic lower back pain. He then read somewhere that this could be precipitated by eating lettuce. He decided to stop eating the stuff and, to his utmost surprise, his pain disappeared. Sceptics may raise their eyebrows. However, lettuce, with every other type of food, is a vast chemical factory. All ideosyncratic reactions are underpinned by a sensitivity to one or other of the naturally occurring chemicals in food. One might think, for example, that there could be nothing simpler than a potato, yet what makes a potato a potato (besides water and cellulose) is an amazing cocktail of 150 different chemicals, including arsenic, nitrates, tannin, oxalic acid and the alkaloid also found in deadly nightshade! However unlikely the lettuce-lumbago syndrome may seem, it is possible that it could be due to a sensitivity to one of the chemicals found in lettuce.

Although allergic reactions to certain foodstuffs are not uncommon (I know a poor arthritis sufferer whose permitted diet consists solely of cod and cauliflower), most of us can eat and enjoy a great variety of foodstuffs. There are exceptions: if my father ate bananas for supper, he suffered cramp in his right calf muscle at night. What is more, I have inherited this tendency. Bernard Levin, writing in *The Times*, said that bananas had this effect on him also. I wrote to him and he replied: 'We banana-phobes must stick together!'

I once had a colleague who took no pleasure in what he ate. He regarded eating as taking fuel on board. However, the vast interest in cooking programmes on the television testifies to the fact that most of us do enjoy food.

> Meat and fish and cheeses
> Sausages galore,
> Fruit and veg. and good wine
> Who could ask for more?
> Puddings, cakes and pastries
> Add their special zest,
> Of all life's many pleasures,
> Eating is the best.

A.L.M.

CHAPTER 7: LIMESTONE

Stalactites and Old Churches

Introduction

I PICKED UP A WHITE PIECE OF ROCK from the path on which I was walking towards the lecture room. I was conducting a course for science teachers in the Murree Hills in Northern Pakistan. The lesson was to be a special occasion because, in addition to the teachers, a class of pupils was to be sitting in front and an Inspector of Education at the back. He was a rather fierce looking man, short and with a small pointed beard. The teachers seemed to be rather in awe of him – but the pupils didn't know who he was. The main object of my course (sponsored by the British Council) was to try to show the teachers that science could be taught in other ways than by lecturing, learning by heart and examinations. At this time efforts were being made not only to modernise school science but to improve teaching methods. Pupils were encouraged to ask questions, to think for themselves and to discover and find out – both in the laboratory and in books. This was very different from the way science had been taught – especially in Asia. To start the lesson I asked the class what they thought this piece of white rock might be? They had already studied chemistry for a couple of years and had heard of limestone. Before any of them could reply, the Inspector shouted from the back, 'It is silica!'. 'Thank you', I said and, to the class, 'The Inspector says it is silica. Can you think of anything else it might be?' No response of course. 'Could it be something you have already studied?' One shy response came: 'Could it be limestone?' 'Maybe', I said, 'But how can we tell? Can you think of a reaction of limestone that you know about which we could use as a test?' After more such heavy-going discussion, we decided to add a few drops of acid to the stone: if it were limestone it would 'fizz' as the carbon dioxide gas came off; if it were silica it wouldn't. I got a pupil to come forward and carry out the test in front of the class. There was a lot of bubbling on the stone, easily visible to all the class. The Inspector had been wrong. I felt very sorry for him and embarrassed that he would lose face, but I had to say, 'Well, it looks as if the Inspector was wrong'. (A pity he shouted out in the first place!)

I have long been interested in rocks and the chemical compounds, 'minerals', of which they consist. Living in the Weald of Sussex, I had often studied the chalk strata and the layers of sandstones, coloured yellow, brown and red, that lie below the chalk. I used to take students on a cross-country route, starting from the local clay and crossing the sandstone layers southwards to the Chalk Downs. Here, in old chalk quarries, we saw the layers of flint and of pyrite, found the fossil remains of bivalve shells and, just once, a shark's tooth. For many years I accompanied my friend Frank Blyth, a senior lecturer in Geology at

Imperial College, London, on field trips. Some of these were to the Malvern Hills, where excellent exposures of a great variety of rocks, covering many geological periods, are to be found. Some were trips to the Shropshire hills, where Frank was studying basalts and other rocks that had intruded from the molten magna deep in the earth's crust. These had emerged through deposits of younger sediments as lava flows and minor intrusions, and had often heated the sediments so strongly as to change their chemical composition.

I have hammered at many types of rock on these expeditions and brought back specimens to study. From some I have cut a slice with a diamond saw, mounted it on a glass microscope slide, ground down the slice to a transparent slip, and examined and photographed it through a polarising microscope. I had even interested some of my students in the chemistry of minerals.

I suppose the most outstanding student was a Cornish boy named Clark who already had a keen interest in minerals. He would set off on his bicycle with maps, hammer and hand-lens in his rucksack on a camping tour of Devon and Cornwall that might last a week or two. His collection was of such interest that he arranged his mineral specimens in a show case at school – all labelled of course. I asked the Keeper of Minerals at the Natural History Museum to give a talk at the school and to look at Clark's collection. He was quite impressed but got into an argument with Clark over a certain specimen of malachite, the green copper mineral. 'That didn't come from Cornwall', he said, 'It's typical of one from the copper belt in Northern Rhodesia' (Zambia). Clark insisted that he had collected it near Camborne in Cornwall. Before they came to blows, I suggested that perhaps a retired miner from Zambia had brought it back, and that his widow had thrown it out on to a mining tip! Whatever the truth, the Keeper was sufficiently impressed by Clark's enthusiasm to let him work in the Museum during the school holidays. Unfortunately Clark's keenness was such that he stayed on in the Museum long after closing time and one evening when he left he set off the security alarm. The police came and Clark, after trying to explain his presence in the Museum after hours, was fined £25. This did not prevent him from eventually becoming a university lecturer in Mineralogy.

I have chosen, somewhat arbitrarily, two rocks to illustrate how chemistry plays a part in their usefulness to man:

(i) *Limestone* – to illustrate its uses, and also how a knowledge of chemistry by builders in past centuries would have enabled them to use chalk rock so that the buildings were more resistant to weathering.

(ii) *Granite* – which is also subject to weathering, but to a lesser extent than limestone. An understanding of the effects of weather on one of the minerals in granite enabled a war-time problem in electrical equipment to be solved. Lastly, when granite is broken down to its constituent minerals over long periods of time, minor but valuable constituents are set free and are mined for use by man. Cassiterite, the ore of tin, is one.

Limestone

Limestone is one of the commonest and most useful of rocks. There are many varieties of limestone, but all are composed largely of the mineral 'calcite', which is the chemical 'calcium carbonate'. Much limestone is used as a building stone. Marble also consists of the mineral calcite – it is limestone that has been re-crystallised by heat somewhere in the earth's crust.

Limestone is not only used as a building stone – great quantities are converted in lime kilns into quicklime. This is used for making cement, in several chemical industries and, after converting to slaked lime by adding water, for 'sweetening the soil' in agriculture. Quicklime reacts strongly with water, generating much heat, and it was because of this property that it found an unusual use during World War II, as described below.

Tropical Packaging

During the 1939–45 war in South East Asia, much equipment was sent out to the armies in the tropics. To try to prevent equipment such as radio sets from deteriorating in the damp air, a bag of silica gel was included inside the packaging to keep the contents dry. The silica gel had to be imported from the USA – not easy in wartime – so a substitute was sought. In the Admiralty Research Department we looked in chemical databooks to find out which substance absorbed the highest percentage of water. A bright young graduate came up with magnesium perchlorate – but how do you get hold of tons of that in a hurry? So we settled for quicklime, which will react with over 30% of its weight of water. There were various practical problems to be solved, e.g. where did we get the quicklime and how did we package it so that it did not contaminate the equipment?

I was sent to Derbyshire to visit two large limestone quarries where there were also kilns for converting it to lime. At one of these I was given a lift by a man from the Ministry of Agriculture. He warned me off one of the companies because his Ministry had tested samples and found that the chunks of limestone coming out of their kilns were only converted into quicklime for a depth of one inch or so into the lump. 'When you get to the next kiln', he said, 'give the chunks of stuff that come out of it a good kick and see if more than the surface layers break off'. I did this and the Admiralty bought from the second lime-maker.

The drying agent included in the packages of equipment had to be wrapped in a little bag, so to get the quicklime into suitably sized pieces we had it made into pellets. Getting the use of a pelleting machine was tricky – all had been requisitioned by the Ministry of Health for use with medicines. However, when I spoke with the Medical Director General, and asked him if he wanted his medicines to reach the tropics in good condition, he agreed to let us use two pelleting machines.

The pellets were quite big – about 2 cm in diameter. We decided to pack them in sealed brown paper bags. We knew that brown paper is permeable to the water vapour in the air, so damp air from outside could reach the quicklime. When the pellets of quicklime reacted with the moisture, the slaked lime produced fell away from the surface of the pellets, thus exposing fresh surfaces of quicklime. The slaked lime remained in the bag, so the equipment was protected from it. Samples passed their test, so all was ready. Then VJ Day arrived and the Second World War was over. The two tons of pellets we had made suffered the ignominious fate of being shovelled into boilers of ships that were being 'cocooned' for storage.

Chalk Rock

Chalk is a form of limestone and consists largely of calcium carbonate. Large areas of England and France are chalk. The well known cliffs of Dover expose the white rock in all its glory. The chalk deposits were formed about 200 million years ago when tiny aquatic plants (algae) lived and died in the Cretaceous seas. Quite recently (1999) the sea between South Devon and the Isles of Scilly, when viewed from outer space, was found to be white. The milk effect was said to be caused by billions of minute pieces of calcium carbonate being shed from the algae (called *Emiliano Huxleyi*) as they died.

Chalk is not very soluble in water, but water containing carbon dioxide is acidic (carbonic acid) and reacts chemically with chalk, making it more soluble (see *Glossary*). The chalk rock is as permeable to water as a sponge, so where it is also exposed to carbon dioxide from the air, its structure is weakened, cracks develop and great chunks of chalk cliffs fall into the sea.

Many years ago, chalk rock was used in certain areas to build walls and churches. Some of the stones cut from the chalk rock have lasted for hundreds of years, but others have weathered and crumbled badly. Why was there this difference? This problem provides a good example of where a knowledge and understanding of chemistry would have helped. The key lies in the fact that, as the blocks of chalk, saturated with a solution of calcium carbonate in carbonic acid solution, dry out, the calcium carbonate is re-deposited at the surface of the block in the form of a hard crystalline, protective layer. If the block is then built into the building without further cutting, this layer will protect it against the weather. But if the stone is cut to shape *after* it has dried out, the protective layer will be removed and the block will crumble under the action of air and rain.

This solubility of limestone in carbonic acid is also responsible for the creation of caves in limestone rocks and the formation of stalactites and stalagmites.

Flint

Those who are familiar with chalk areas will know that layers of flint in the form of nodules are often found in the chalk. Whole villages in the vicinity are sometimes built of flints, but why is the flint invariably in the form of nodules?

At a meeting of the Geologists Association held in Cornwall many years ago, I asked an eminent mineralogist why the flint had formed in nodules? 'Well', he said, 'there are many geologists in England but they are not evenly spread over the country but gathered together here in a kind of 'nodule', and that was the only explanation I got!

Flint consists of silica derived from skeletons of sponges. These once lived in waters like the Wealden Lake during

Cretaceous times (about 200 million years ago). When the dead sponges fell to the bottom of the lake, their silica skeletons gradually absorbed water and became jelly-like – their structure was that of a gel – similar to that of the silica gel we know today as used as a drying agent in packaging. This form of silica gel is hard, having been heated to remove all the water. When it re-absorbs water, if it absorbs enough, it eventually becomes jelly-like. The lumps of gel from the ancient sponges got buried deeper and deeper and, as the temperature and pressure rose, the water was expelled from them and they became flint – a solidified gel. The centres of hollow flints often contain sponge spicules – evidence of their origin. Fossils of small molluscs are sometimes found embedded in the surfaces of flints.

Pyrites

A different kind of nodule is sometimes found in chalk. They are roughly spherical, brown in colour and, if broken open, are found to consist of brass-coloured crystalline material. This is a mineral very similar to 'fools' gold', iron pyrites. The yellow crystals grew out from the centre of each nodule as radiating needle-like forms making recognisable crystal facets at the surface. They are sometimes found loose on the chalk downs and referred to as 'meteorites' – which they are not.

These nodules have played an important role in the history of chemistry. In the 15th century the alchemist Glauber obtained sulphuric acid from them. He described the process in the following picturesque manner: 'After allowing the nodules to weather for a few weeks, add much faire rain water, decant and allow the water to evaporate for some time. After many days little green stones will shoot'. These were crystals of green vitriol (iron sulphate), which was formed by the action of the air and water during the weathering of the iron pyrites.

The preparation of 'oil of vitriol' was described thus: 'If you get the mineral called Green Vitriol, pray to God for understanding and wisdom and after you have calcined it' (i.e. heated it) 'increase the fire. There then comes in the form of a white spirit of vitriol, in the manner of a horrid fume or wind, and cometh into the Receiver ...' This 'oil of vitriol', now known as sulphuric acid, is a very corrosive liquid. Details of the chemical reactions are given in the *Glossary*.

My students often repeated these experiments with nodules collected on the South Downs and obtained beautiful green crystals of iron sulphate. They then heated some in a test tube and obtained a few oily, corrosive drops of sulphuric acid as distillate. Vitriol, whose green crystals look like glass, derives its name from the Latin for 'glassy'. It is amusing to note that the adjective 'vitriolic', as applied to someone's temper, means 'fiery' like the acid, not 'placid' like the glassy crystals. The word 'vitriolic' thus owes its meaning to a chemical reaction!

CHAPTER 8: GRANITE

A source of valuable minerals

WHEN I WAS WORKING at Imperial College, London, I often had a sandwich lunch with my friend Frank Blyth and we were sometimes joined by his Head of Department, Professor Read, a charming Scot. Granite was his special interest: 'Not all rocks known as "granite" are true granites', he would tell us. 'True granite is a primary rock that has crystallised deep in the earth's crust from the liquid magma there.' Dartmoor is a well-known outcrop of granite and Frank and I often went on geological trips there. I asked the Professor whether Dartmoor was made of true granite. 'Oh yes', he said, 'Dartmoor is a large mass of granite, pushed up and exposed at the surface, a true primary rock. Most of Scotland is usually said to be composed of granite but I regret to have to say that the rocks of the Highlands are not granite at all.' This was a blow to me – my mother was a Scot!

'The rocks of Glencoe and most of the Scottish hills are composed of rocks that look like granite, but are not primary rocks. In fact, when examined closely, they show patterns that suggest that they have not always been as we find them today. Some were sediments, others were igneous rock, but all have been changed by heat and

pressure in the depths of the earth – their original constituents have been re-crystallised and changed to the
minerals that constitute a granite plus some more. In many
ways they look like granite, are as hard as granite and are
often used for building and road stones – but they are not
true granite. They are called migmatites and are usually
built up of rocks that have undergone a metamorphosis.
And so it was, in a small room over a sandwich lunch, I
learnt that things in the world of geology are not as simple
as I had once thought.

If you look at a freshly fractured piece of granite rock
on Dartmoor, you will see that the colour from the surface
inwards for a depth of a few centimetres is brown –
whereas the bulk of the rock is a mottled grey colour. This
is not a superficial change – the rock itself has been
changed. How can this happen? The hymn 'Rock of Ages'
inclines us to think of rocks as eternal, but this is not so.
All types of rock are subject to attack by the weather. Even
granite is slowly worn away at its surfaces. Greek philosophers used this observation as an argument for the
smallness of atoms – only by consisting of very small
particles could the rocks be worn away so smoothly and
slowly.

I have already discussed the weathering of limestone,
but granite is a very different stuff. It consists of three
main minerals: quartz, felspar and ferromagnesium minerals such as mica. Quartz is a simple mineral; the other
minerals, felspar and mica, are more complex. All have a
layer-like structure. The backbone of this structure consists
of chains of silicon, aluminium and oxygen atoms. These
are lightly bonded together by metal ions such as potas-

sium and iron. This bonding is weaker than that which connects the aluminium, silicon and oxygen atoms within the chain (for the formulae, see *Glossary*). When these minerals are attacked by water the inter-layer ions react to form soluble substances. As a result of this, the felspars become soft and easily removed by rain and the other minerals are also decomposed and yield iron oxide, which stains the rock brown. This is what is happening to the outer parts of granite under the influence of the weather and over a lengthy period.

A knowledge of the chemistry of these minerals helped to solve a problem that arose during World War II. Here is the story: When radio sets were used in the tropical jungles of Burma, it was found that the insulation in many cases broke down. To separate two points in a radio set that had a difference in voltage, insulators made of small rods of a substance containing mica were often used. Under conditions of high humidity at night, a conducting film of moisture was formed on the surface of the insulators. This film contained a trace of potash (an alkali) dissolved from the mica. It dried off during the hot day but more was formed during the humid night. The film was quite a good conductor, causing an electrical leakage between the two ends of the insulator. A knowledge of the structure of the mica enabled me to solve this problem. I told the manufacturer to boil the little rods of insulating material in water, wash and dry them and then use them in the radio sets and they would then continue to act as insulators. His reaction was rather like that of Naaman in the Bible when he was told to cure his leprosy by washing seven times in the River Jordan. 'He went away in a rage.'

The suggested treatment was too simple for him to take it seriously. However, the small insulators were washed as suggested and it was found that the treatment was completely effective.

How could that be? The key lies in the structure of the mica. Once the layer of potassium ions has been removed by washing, the backbone layers of alumino-silicate are exposed. These do not react with water, so the insulating properties of the material are restored.

The action of water on the surface of many other minerals has been studied and the results published in the *British Medical Journal*. The most active mineral, by a long way, was asbestos. As is well known, asbestos dust causes diseases of the lung, partly because of the mechanical effect of the minute fibres but also because the mineral reacts with water to give a strong alkali. The use of asbestos in many applications (such as heat insulation) is now banned. However, asbestos card and sheeting is harmless – it is only when it is sawn or drilled, or when wear and friction release fibres that become airborne, that it is dangerous.

Breakdown of Rocks

The weathering of the surface of granite is nothing compared with what happens when the weathering penetrates into the body of the rock! To see what happens there, we have to go back in geological time. Then we find that whole masses of rock have been decomposed and washed away by streams and rivers and deposited as what are known as alluvial deposits. From these can be obtained some of the constituents of the original rocks – those constituents that are tough and have survived all this physical and chemical battering. In certain cases these minerals constitute only a small fraction of the original rock but the weathering processes have separated them out and led to their accumulation in certain areas. Well known examples are gold and tin ore.

Tinstone

In my role as careers master I visited Nigeria. The tin mining companies there were short of mining engineers and wanted to interest school leavers in tin mining. I was put up in a company guest house at Jos. Jos is on the Bauchi plateau in Northern Nigeria. The climate is pleasant, so that those who work in hot sticky Lagos escape to Jos for a break when they can. The house could accommodate about ten guests, but, apart from a number of Nigerian servants, I was there on my own. At breakfast I sat at the top of an otherwise empty table. Two white-clad, red-fezzed Nigerian servants stood behind me. Plates of food came and vanished silently. When I had finished eating, a cigarette appeared from over my right shoulder and a lighted match from the left. I do not normally smoke, but politeness forced me to do so on such occasions. I got on friendly terms with the Nigerian chief steward and we had an interesting conversation about a child's birth soon to occur in the servants' quarters. When the baby was born, I asked after its health etc. He replied: 'It is a boy. He is heavy and fine – but very *black!*' There are shades of black even among 'black' races.

The days were occupied with visits to the open-cast mine and to the minerals separation plant. Open-cast mining is more like quarrying than mining. Enormous mechanical forks and shovels excavate the earth in large portions at one time. The machines are mounted on 'feet' several yards long and these can move the excavator step by step to fresh sites. The material excavated was sandy in texture, the tin ore it contained being in the form of black dense grains mixed in with the rest of the sandy material. The traditional method of 'panning' (*photograph*) can be used to separate the tin ore and is adapted for use on a large scale. The equipment consists of a wooden structure look-ing like a large open stairway. The sand is washed down the staircase by a gentle stream of water (*photograph*). The heavy grains of tin ore remain on the 'steps', the light sand grains being washed away. Workers, protected from the heat by broad-brimmed, pretty hats, shovel the black ore that collects on the steps into sacks, which are then taken to the separation plant. These sacks of black ore are valu-able and worth stealing, so the plant is protected by barbed wire and by lights at night. The black ore is separated into a number of minerals such as columbite, garnet, zircon etc, but of course the main product is cassiterite, the ore from which the metal tin is obtained, and this is sent, under guard, to the refineries elsewhere to be reduced to the metal.

About ten years later I was to visit Malaysia and see more modern equipment being used for tin mining. This visit was by courtesy of the Anglo-Oriental Tin Mining Company. I had travelled up from Singapore overnight and was entertained to breakfast by the manager of the company. 'Because of the tropical heat in this country, we find it advisable to take salt tablets at breakfast', he said. These were too much for me and I had to leave the table fast. I have never taken salt tablets since, but have never suffered from the heat in spite of this omission.

The manager arranged for me to visit some tin mines. The first was a vast old quarry-like mine in Tronoh. The tin ore, consisting of heavy black grains dispersed in alluvial sand deposits, is dug out by hand and by mechanical shovels. We also visited a modern mine which used a 3,000-ton dredge that floats on a huge pond and scoops up alluvial deposits from the cliff at the edges of the pond by means of a moving chain of buckets. On board, the dredge sorts out its 'catch' into the valuable black grains of tin ore and the useless mud and white sand. This it spews out at its rear end while shaking tablets concentrate the valuable tin ore in its central compartment. Costing over £1 million each, these dredges are like floating excavators and mineral seperation plants all in one. (*Photograph*).

Tin country is characterised in Malaysia by the patchwork of old mining pools. Some of the oldest, such as those at Taiping, have been turned into lakes and landscaped into pleasant gardens. Others are being brought into cultivation. Even the unsightly and useless stretches of quartz sand can be made to yield a crop eventually by means of a clever biological trick: certain creepers can find enough moisture and nutrients to grow on the sand and these form a soil which, after a few years, is suitable for other plants to root in and grow on. I have seen such creepers growing. In this way the land that has been lost through mining operations is slowly recovered (*photograph*).

Tin, and therefore the ore from which it is obtained, is

not in so much demand these days. The good old tin can no longer uses tin as a lining. This is now provided by plastics. Other uses for tin have been developed. One of these, where a compound of tin is used as a constituent of anti-fouling paint to protect ships' hulls from marine growth, had to be banned as it was alleged to poison fish too.

When I was in the Admiralty during World War Two we did a lot of experiments on anti-fouling paints. These were used on the outside surface of the keels of ships where various types of marine organisms would grow and sometimes build into rough layers in quite a short time. These, of course, slowed down the ships and had to be removed periodically. The application of anti-fouling paints could greatly reduce these growths. I remember that we had hundreds of samples of steel plates suspended just below water level from wooden battens and coated with a number of anti-fouling paints. The research work was carried out in the bay off Emsworth in Hampshire and it was the unpleasant duty of a research worker to wade out through several feet of sea water every few days and report on the state of the plates.

Tin is, of course, still a major constituent of bronze (as it has been since before the Iron Age) and of other alloys such as pewter and solder.

Some industries that extract tin from rocks containing tin ore as part of their contents don't wait for nature to cause the rocks to break up. They crush the rocks up in stages, finishing by grinding them to a powder. This is then dispersed in water and a chemical added that gives rise to a froth, like washing-up liquid. Air is bubbled through the mass and finely powdered metallic ore collects on the surfaces of the bubbles, which are floated off as a foam (*photograph*).

> The cave man used rocks as his home
> Out from which he could hunt, fish and roam.
> We blast them and crush them,
> Add liquids to mush them,
> And float off their ores in a foam.

G.V.P.

CHAPTER 9: FOSSILS

The wonderful life of long ago

I ONCE PURCHASED A BOOK called *Wonderful Life* (by S.J. Gould). It was not about what I expected, but was about very ancient fossil remains dating back over 550 million years from beyond the Cambrian Period to muds containing microscopic worm-like creatures. These may be 'wonderful' in their own way but not the 'wonderful life' I was expecting to read about.

As I've said several times, this is not a textbook. If it were, a section on fossils would occupy many volumes. No, I am writing about interesting experiences I have had involving a few 'stuffs', in this case fossils. My first experience, an exciting one but with a disappointing outcome, was when I was with my friend, Frank Blyth, on one of his geological expeditions in the Malvern Hills. We were visiting a small but historic quarry where fossils of some of the earliest forms of life had been found – trilobites from the Cambrian era some 500–600 million years ago. It was called the Comfrey quarry and nestled under Caer Caradoc Hill on the other side of the north-south road by the Long Mynd. Sadly all we found were small traces of the trilobites – no doubt all that had been left by previous fossil-hunters.

Some years ago, this area was visited by members of the Geologists Association, who were to be guided by the elderly vicar of Church Stretton, an amateur geologist with great local knowledge. They assembled at 2 p.m. on the day as planned but the vicar did not turn up. A messenger went to the old vicarage to find him. There he was, in his carpet slippers, practising the cello. 'The geologists are waiting for you, sir.' The vicar replied: 'No, they are coming tomorrow, Wednesday'. 'But today is Wednesday, sir.' 'Are you sure? Dearie me, then I am practising the cello for a concert I should have played at last night!'

One of my most exciting finds occurred a bit further south, near Ledbury. I was splitting open pieces of stone of Silurian Age (c 400 million years old) from strata called the Lower Ludlow Mudstone. They contained plenty of fossils of various shapes and sizes. Imagine the thrill of finding in your left hand a perfect mould of a Silurian bivalve, about 1½" across and the cast of the shell in your right hand fitting exactly into the mould. Its name was Atrypo and as I looked at it I felt like telling it: 'I am the first person to look at you in 400 million years'. I had it in my possession until two or three years ago, when I gave it to a young collector.

As I write, I am sitting opposite my fireplace which is made of slabs of Sussex Marble (*photograph*). This is a bluish-grey stone packed with fossils. They look like sections of modern garden snails but in fact they are fossils called *Paludina*, and once lived in the shallow waters of the Wealden lake about 150 million years ago. Some cross sections look just like snails, others have different patterns. They must have perished in some catastrophe and fallen into the mud in their thousands, to be preserved as fossils to decorate the Sussex Marble. The font in Arundel Church is made of it and there are samples in some Sussex churches and in the Horsham Museum.

My slabs of the marble have an interesting history: they were dug up from small outcrops in Broadbridge Heath near Horsham. The quarries belonged to a builders' merchant, one of whose daughters married an old pupil of mine. When he built his house, 'Wild Acre', in Bashurst Copse, Itchingfield, he used slabs of the marble as surrounds for the fireplace in his living room. I had often seen them there and been fascinated by the numerous sections of the fossils. Many years later, at the offices of the Nuffield Foundation where I was working at the time, a new girl secretary appeared one morning. To make her feel at home, I asked her if she had travelled far. I brightened up when she said 'From Horsham', where I had taught at Christ's Hospital for some years. 'How interesting,' I said, 'and whereabouts do you live?' Nowhere you would know – near a village called Itchingfield.' 'Certainly I know it – and whereabouts near Itchingfield?' 'In a small wood called Bashurst Copse.'I held my breath. 'The house is called Wild Acre,' she added. Her parents later asked me to visit her. I went for drinks before lunch the next Sunday. I recognised the house at once, although the living room had been extended and the wall where the fireplace was had been removed. 'What happened to the stone fireplace surround?' I asked. 'Oh, we're just using it as stepping stones to the dustbin.' 'You can't do that!', I protested, and told them about Sussex Marble. 'You can have them, if you like,' her father said. So, for a bottle of whisky, that's how the Sussex Marble came into my possession to adorn my fireplace – a much more dignified resting place for it than on the muddy path to the dustbins.

Readers may be able to add examples they have seen of beautiful fossiliferous marbles. One that should certainly be mentioned is the columns of palaeozoic marble in Durham Cathedral. The patterns are due to great numbers of trilobites in a local rock which must be at least 300 million years old.

Of course, when these living organisms died and were buried in the mud at the bottom of the sea, or by the debris of the land where they had lived, their soft parts soon decayed away – only the skeletons, skulls and teeth have been preserved. The soft parts of, for example, a bivalve shell, are replaced by material derived from the surrounding 'graveyard'. This may be mudstone, fine sandstone, limestone or other materials. I once found a bivalve in Derbyshire that had a little purple crystal near the joint of its two halves. This find was not far from the Blue John mines. I wondered if the centre of the fossil could have contained Blue John, but it was years until I decided to saw it open and see. In fact, about half the cavity was occupied by the mineral, the rest was empty. It was an interesting sample – I wish I hadn't given it away to that young collector! I doubt if he would have realised what a rare sample it was.

The 'Wonderful Life' referred to in Gould's book consists of whole new groups of soft-bodied creatures, mostly less than 5 cm long, buried in such fine-grained mud that their features are preserved in amazing detail. They were discovered in 1909 (the year I was born!) in the 'Burgess

Shale', strata high in the Canadian Rockies on the eastern border of British Columbia. They are about 530 million years old and therefore pre-date all other known fossils. They include an immense variety of creatures. 'Some fifteen to twenty species are not allied with any known group', said Gould. But there are representatives of all four of the major groups of arthropods on earth today: crustaceans (crabs, shrimps etc), chelicerates (spiders, scorpions etc), uniramians (insects etc) and 20 or 30 kinds of arthropod belonging to no modern group – wonderful life indeed! If you want to know more, you can find it, including many pictures and diagrams, buried in this American science writer's book.

> There once was a pleisiosaurus
> Who lived when the earth was all porous.
> It fainted with shame
> When it first heard its name
> And departed long ages before us.

Anon.

Chapter 2 - Rag paper drying in the sun

Chapter 2 - The widespread destruction of forests

Chapter 4 - In places, the oil seeps out of the ground

Chapter 4 - Nebuchadnezzar's burning fiery furnace

Chapter 4 - The oil was taken by pipeline to the coast

Chapter 4 - The nuts grow in clusters on the palm trees

Chapter 8 - The traditional method of panning

Chapter 8 - The heavy grains of tin ore remain on the steps

CHAPTER 10: QUARTZ

What is it doing in your watch?

A VERY SMALL PIECE OF QUARTZ is hiding in your quartz watch – but what is it doing there? In one sentence, it is taking the place of the hairspring and escapement in controlling the accuracy of the watch. Quartz is crystalline silica, and occurs in many forms such as opaque white rocks, transparent 'rock crystals', coloured varieties such as amethyst, rose quartz, citrine, 'smoky' quartz and agate. Of course watches do not contain big crystals – in fact the quartz in watches consists of a very tiny piece cut from special crystals. In what way are they special? Let me explain. When ordinary quartz crystals are examined by X-ray, they are found to have a structure rather like a jigsaw puzzle – little pieces of quartz with a uniform structure are fitted together to make the shape we see. Some natural crystals are made up of bigger units of single crystals than others and these are the ones which are the most suitable from which to cut thin plates of quartz for use in watches and other instruments.

The best crystals come from Brazil, and during World War II both Germany and the UK were importing them across the Atlantic in convoys at great expense. In fact, in 1942, of every £1,000 spent by Britain on imports, £1 went on quartz. Quartz was urgently needed for use in radio and radar instruments, so both German and British scientists were set to work to try to grow single crystals of quartz in the laboratory. By the mid-forties the Germans had succeeded, and soon after the War ended we found out how they had done it. This is the story.

Immediately after the war, Naval Intelligence discovered that a certain Professor Nacken, of Frankfurt University, had achieved some success in growing single crystals of quartz. My colleague in the Admiralty Department of Scientific Research, George Richardson (later Master of Keble College, Oxford) and I were sent off to look for him. The story reads more like a Conan Doyle operation than scientific research (of course there are similarities!). We flew to Frankfurt and located the University. It was largely in ruins but there was a small door in a part of the building that was still standing. We knocked. An elderly woman dressed in black eventually answered but told us that Professor Nacken was no longer there. However, there were a few other professors there and one told us that Nacken had been evacuated to the Black Forest some years back and was working for a firm of watch and instrument makers, Junghaus, well known at the time. We set off to find him.

The Black Forest was in the French zone of occupation and to go there we needed appropriate passes. The Algerian Arab guard at the frontier post, with his white robe and long curved sword, clearly could make nothing of our typewritten passes, but cigarettes were passports to almost anything at that time and we were soon on our way to our destination, Baden Baden. We queued for a billet in the town, having washed under the hot water tap in the central square. The French billeting officer, seeing the 'Royal Navy' flashes on our battle-dresses, dryly remarked 'Ici la mer est très chaude'. A supply of hot water was, in fact, the only comfort there – I shall never forget the taste of acorn coffee or the slice of soggy pudding that substituted for bread.

The watch factory was at the head of a beautiful valley and we interviewed Professor Nacken sitting in an orchard nearby. He was most friendly and very willing to tell us about his research work. He had succeeded in growing quartz crystals by a method he had himself developed, but the biggest crystal so far was only about one centimetre across and had taken three months to grow. He would tell us more later, but far more interesting, he said, were the emeralds. He had a cocoa-tin full of them, beautiful clear green crystals he had grown himself. Most were about three millimetres long but some were nearly a centimetre. He gave me a dozen of the smaller ones and I gave eight to the Natural History Museum in London, where, no doubt, they may still be seen.

Nacken gave us all the technical details for growing quartz crystals. His best crystal had been sent to Berlin for tests on its properties. It was in the hands of a certain Dr Bechman of the Reichspost Research Institute in Berlin. A month or so later we set out to look for him. When we reached Berlin, after driving along the autobahn through the Russian zone of occupation, we found that Dr Bechman had not registered with the military authorities, so his address was not known to them. They suggested that we should call on all the Bechmans listed in the telephone directory, of which the latest was dated 1942. There were three pages of Bechmans – fourteen had science degrees. We started to call on them systematically. The fourth address was that of a flat over a damaged shop. As the occupant opened the door, I saw some fine quartz crystals on the mantelpiece of the room facing me. Dr Bechman was very friendly and willingly showed us the synthetic quartz crystal grown by Professor Nacken. We discussed it at some length – yes, it had identical properties to those of natural quartz. We returned to England with all the electrical data and other details about the crystal.

Quartz in Pint Pots

A few years later I was asked to read a paper on Synthetic Minerals to a Faraday Society conference held in the Royal Institution in London. It was here that the famous scientists, Sir Humphry Davy and Michael Faraday, and others after them had made many important discoveries – Davy isolated sodium and potassium, Faraday discovered electromagnetism, Sir William Bragg and his son, Sir Lawrence, developed the use of X-rays in the study of crystals. I felt quite thrilled to read a paper in such an august place.

I do not like talking about something of which I have no first-hand experience so, as I had details of Nacken's method of growing quartz crystals, I thought I would try to grow some. I was teaching at Christ's Hospital, where the facilities were just capable of enabling me to try to do so. The experiments involved the use of a small steel autoclave which would have to stand high pressures of up to 1,000 atmospheres. There was a slight possibility that it might explode. The work was done in a small laboratory at the top of the Science building. The boys referred to it as 'the bomb room'. The autoclave often leaked but was never in any danger of exploding. Over a period of time we carried out fourteen experiments, obtained some minute quartz crystals about one millimetre long, and made some slides of them to illustrate my paper. Before the meeting, waiting in the foyer of the Royal Institution, I was delighted to see Dr Bechman standing there too. I told him that most of my paper would be connected with synthetic quartz and that I proposed to project some slides of crystals I had grown. He put his hand in his waistcoat pocket and said: 'You may like to show this too'. It was the original crystal that Nacken had sent to him and which I had first seen in Berlin.

After the conference, three of the metallurgists present offered to make me a bigger and better autoclave, and all three did so. We chose to use the one made by Vickers-Armstrong out of high tensile steel. With this we did over a hundred experiments and eventually grew a crystal of quartz almost as big as that grown by Nacken. This is how we did it:-

Our autoclave was about 150 cm high and about 50 cm in diameter. We placed some crushed silica in the bottom of the 'bomb' and a seed crystal of quartz was put near the top. The solvent, mostly water, was then added and the bomb closed, positioned in the furnace and heated from the bottom. The solution would dissolve some silica and convection currents would carry it to the top, where it was cooler. Silica would deposit as quartz on the seed crystal – or so we hoped! Several factors had to be just right for this to happen.

To get high rates of growth, it is desirable to use as high a temperature as possible, but there is a limit to this because if the temperature is raised beyond a certain value, known as the 'critical temperature' (about 370°C), the water can only exist as vapour and not as liquid. We needed to have liquid water in the bomb to carry the silica in solution from the bottom to the top. (I cannot imagine that the silica could be conveyed by water vapour.) So the temperature had to be less than 370 degrees.

There was a second important factor: if the bomb was filled only to say 50 per cent, as the temperature was raised, the water was all eventually converted to vapour. In order for it to be largely filled with liquid at the operating temperature, it was necessary to fill it up to about 60 per cent at the start.

After setting up the equipment, we would leave it working on its own, never entering the 'bomb room'. When we decided to terminate the 'run' we would switch off the furnace and leave it to cool. Then came the difficult bit – opening the bomb. Its circular lid was connected to the body by a mild steel ring carefully ground into both surfaces. The lid was held down by six high-tensile steel bolts. Because the high pressures developed inside the bomb (up to 1,000 atmospheres) put a great strain on the bolts, their threads became distorted and they were extremely difficult to undo. We had a special long-handed spanner, but even so we sometimes had to saw off one of the bolts – another very hard job.

You can imagine our state of excitement as we struggled

to open the bomb – something between optimistic hope and resigned disappointment. Out of over 100 'runs', only about 20 yielded useful results. The rest usually failed because the bomb had leaked. In our best run, which lasted over two weeks, we grew a crystal of about 1.5 cm in length.

In England, the work of growing quartz crystals was being done by the General Electric Company. It so happened that the scientist in charge had been a pupil at Christ's Hospital. After the Faraday Society Conference, he visited me at the school to discuss our work. He told me that they had been exploring the effect of various additives to the water. I showed him Nacken's results on this subject, which indicated that the nature of the additive was unimportant. Nacken's results clearly showed that the important factor was the extent to which the autoclave was filled with water. Maybe this was the key factor that, a few months later, enabled GEC to be successful in growing quartz crystals. Crystals of about 5 cm in length were grown in about three weeks.

Our next ambition was to grow a crystal of amethyst, the familiar purple gemstone. Amethyst consists of quartz coloured by certain impurities, namely iron and potassium. The colour is caused by a distortion of the quartz crystal lattice by a combination of an iron atom and a potassium atom substituting for a silicon atom. This particular combination can produce coloured quartz crystals, including amethyst. Unfortunately for us, amethyst crystals lose their colour on heating to temperatures above about 350°C – too low for us to grow them in our 'bomb'. However, we did not know this at the time, so we tried putting a little iron and potassium salts into the bomb. To our surprise, the crystal that grew was coloured green! We searched the Christ's Hospital collection of mineral specimens and were quite excited to find a large crystalline specimen of quartz which included a green band in the otherwise colourless quartz crystals. The green crystal we had grown is included in a showcase in the school, which gives a short account of our experiments on growing quartz crystals.

Now let us ask how quartz fulfils its function in clocks and watches. Quartz has a property (possessed by only a few other substances) known as 'piezoelectricity'. This was discovered by Michael Faraday in the mid-nineteenth century. What is this property? I used to demonstrate it to my students in the following manner. I had a slice of quartz crystal about one inch square and about 1/10th of an inch thick. This was placed on the bench sandwiched between two pieces of copper foil. These were connected by two wires to the terminals of a neon lamp. When the quartz sandwich was smartly tapped with a soft headed hammer (or with my fist!) the neon lamp lit up momentarily. This showed that the quartz slice, when compressed, produced a voltage between its two faces. This is the phenomenon known as piezoelectricity. The reverse process occurs – when a voltage difference is applied across the slice of quartz it contracts: if the voltage is reversed it expands. If the voltage is an alternating one, the quartz slice vibrates. There is one more step needed to explain how this phenomenon is used to control the timing of a watch accurately.

A slice of quartz cut to a certain thickness will vibrate

with a certain frequency – if it is thicker, it will vibrate more slowly, etc. In this way, it is like a pendulum – the longer the pendulum, the slower will be the period of swing. If the pendulum is given a little push at the end of each swing it will swing more widely – we say that it is 'resonating' with the frequency of the 'pushes'. So it is with the quartz slice – if the frequency of the alternating voltage applied to it is the same as the natural frequency of the vibration of the slice, it will resonate, i.e. it will vibrate more strongly than it would if any other frequency were applied to it.

In a quartz watch the crystal controls the frequency, thus ensuring the accuracy of timing, just as the hairspring and escapement do in other watches. For accurate timing, the dimensions of the quartz must be just right.

As we know, quartz watches need a battery to operate. This battery drives a tiny electric motor which moves the hands of the watch. It also generates an alternating voltage which is applied to the quartz crystal. Until recently the battery in a watch had to be replaced periodically, but now designs have been made in which the battery is re-chargeable within the watch. This is done either by mechanical means, as in an automatic watch, or by a photoelectric surface that harnesses the sun's energy to keep the battery charged.

Now I am told by a large watch-making company that all quartz used in watches and other instruments is cut from *synthetic* crystals. Somehow that gives me a nice warm feeling inside!

CHAPTER 11: GLASS

The solid that we used to think was a liquid

FAMILIAR THOUGH GLASS MAY BE, it is in fact most extraordinary stuff. It behaves in a way that other solids do not. Solids melt at a definite temperature – ice at 0°C, sugar at 185°C, gold at 1063°C etc, but when glass is heated it gradually softens, then becomes a sticky liquid and eventually will flow like treacle. On cooling, it will gradually solidify again. Because it behaves like this, it used to be referred to as a 'supercooled liquid'. But it is not a liquid – as you will be aware: when you drop a tumbler on the floor it either breaks or bounces. If you have ever pushed hard at a window pane, you will know that glass is not a liquid. We call it an 'amorphous solid' – 'amorphous' = without form. Its constituent particles are not arranged in any particular pattern, as they are in crystalline solids like sugar or salt or ice. All the same it CAN crystallise, i.e. the particles it is made of can arrange themselves in a pattern and then the glass is said to 'de-vitrify'. Some ancient glass has been found like this. I have some specimens of glass from a factory I visited that had 'gone wrong'. One is milky rather than clear glass; another has a few lines of beautifully formed crystals inside it. I also have a specimen of a volcanic glass (a rock called 'obsidian' – similar to that of which the Giants' Causeway in Northern Ireland consists) that is mostly glass but which has started to grow crystalline from a number of points from which radiating needles have spread out to make circular crystalline areas on the surfaces.

One reason glass was referred to as 'supercooled liquid' was that some panes of glass in ancient buildings are thicker at the bottom than at the top. I have seen such panes in the windows of the famous Painted Hall in the Royal Naval College, Greenwich. It was assumed that the glass had slowly flowed down over the centuries. However, lately it has been shown by an Australian physicist, doing theoretical calculations on the known particulate structure of glass, that it would take at least 10 million years for these panes to have flowed as they seem to have. So we need some other explanation – if the calculation was correct!

For centuries flat pieces of glass have been made as follows: the glass blower dips a long hollow tube into molten glass and gathers up a blob on the end of the tube. He then blows down the tube and the molten glass is expanded into a bubble or sometimes into a cylinder by using a cylindrical wet wooden mould. When cool, the mould is opened and the hollow cylinder of glass scratched with a diamond along its length and broken into two. Each half cylinder is placed on a hot plate which causes it to flatten out into a 'pane'. I have seen this done with red glass, as described later. These panes, whether made by the cylinder or bubble method, are not of uniform thickness. This would account for the fact that the window panes at Greenwich are thicker at the bottom than the top

– they were made like that! (Why the thick end was put at the bottom by those who made the windows is anybody's guess – but I think that seems to be the natural thing to do.)

For making large sheets of glass the molten material is allowed to flow on to the surface of a bed of molten tin. When cool and the glass has solidified, it is then removed as a sheet with flat faces – it sounds easier than it no doubt is!

As you know, glass can be cut into various shapes, such as prisms, circles, lenses etc, and can also be carved into beautiful patterns, as on wine glasses, chandeliers and other objects, referred to as 'cut glass'. These are often referred to as 'crystal' but, from a scientific point of view, this is incorrect. The glass, as I have already said, is not crystalline in structure – it is amorphous and it is this that enables it to be cut into an infinity of beautiful objects. If one attempts to cut a crystal, it will cleave along one of its natural cleavage directions, e.g. a crystal of common salt will split into cubes. Diamonds are shaped into gem-stones by being split by the jeweller along certain directions natural to the diamond crystal.

So glass is a very special solid. I am supposed to be telling you about its chemistry, but in fact the properties that make it 'glassy' have more to do with its physical state, as described above, than with its chemical composition. However, the principal constituents of common glass are three chemicals: silica, limestone and soda-ash (which is sodium carbonate). All these are compounds of high melting point, but together make mixtures that soften at much lower temperatures. The process seems to have been known before the Egyptian civilisation. Primitive beads, often coloured, have been made from glass since time immemorial. Maybe glass was discovered when Arabs kindled fires in the sandy desert. The sand is mostly silica and often mixed with debris from limestone rocks. The soda could have come from the salt lakes that are found in the Rift Valley. I have seen one, Lake Magardi, which is covered with a layer of soda crystals several feet thick (*photograph*).

When heated together to temperatures of about 1200°C, silica, limestone and soda ash produce a glassy material consisting of calcium and sodium silicates. Glass for making many objects in common use today consists of:

72% silica (from sand)
11% calcium oxide (from limestone)
13% sodium oxide (from soda ash)
and about 4% of various other ingredients.

Such soda lime glass is easy to make and shape and is reasonably strong. Other chemicals are added to make special glasses.

Lead glass, for example, contains about 25% of lead oxide and is particularly bright and sparkling glass. Because lead compounds are toxic under certain conditions, some countries regulate the use of lead in glass making. Instead of lead oxide, a mixture of titanium dioxide with barium oxide is used. This glass melts at a lower temperature than lead glass and so is easier to work with. It is said to have all the visual attractions of lead glass which make it so suitable for making cut glass objects.

Coloured glass, usually referred to as 'stained glass', is

well known for its use in church windows, etc. The colour is produced by including in the melt oxides of various metals: cobalt oxide produces a fine blue glass, copper a green glass etc.

Early this century, coloured glass was used to make instruments that could measure colour. These were first made by a brewer, W. Lovibond, in Salisbury, Wiltshire. Mr Lovibond wanted to measure the colour of his beer to make sure it was the same from year to year. The instrument he invented could match any colour by comparing it with combinations of yellow, blue and red glass of different intensities. The instrument contained 1 cm squares of each coloured glass of an intensity varying from extremely pale up to very dark by uniform steps. By overlapping one slip of glass of each colour, he could match the colour of any substance, solid or liquid. The instruments were called tintometers and can be used for many purposes, e.g. to measure the colours produced by chemical tests such as that used in testing swimming pool water and for maintaining colour standards in the paint industry.

But there was a snag for Mr Lovibond! The blue and yellow glasses could easily be reproduced to exact standards year by year. But the red glass was different. The colour was produced by 'colloidal gold' and Mr Lovibond purchased his supplies from France. Using his own instrument, he found that the colour varied slightly from batch to batch and he could only make use of less than 10% for his standard 'ruby' glass. Later on, in the mid-twentieth century, his technicians tried to make ruby glass themselves but with not much more success.

The trouble arose because it is very difficult to make consistent colours from a colloidal solution. The British scientist Michael Faraday first made colloidal solutions in water of gold. In such solutions, the gold particles are of a special size – bigger than those of solutes in a true solution, yet not as big as suspensions of particles that would settle out. To produce these colloidal solutions, Faraday started with a solution of gold chloride (a soluble salt) and added a substance that would remove the chloride part of the compound, leaving the element gold. Under suitable conditions the gold was produced in a colloidal form which had a fine ruby-red colour. However, the colour varied with the conditions (temperature, concentration of the gold chloride solution, impurities etc) and could be other shades of red – or even yellow or green! The same variations are also found when the gold chloride is dissolved in glass rather than water. However, Messrs Lovibond succeeded in controlling their conditions of manufacture of red glass to an extent that enabled them to use over 25% of the product, which was better than 10% anyway! The rest was re-cycled.

Glass has innumerable uses, which the reader will know as much about as I do. However, there is one use I would like to write about because when I heard the explanation of how it worked, I couldn't believe it.

Reactolite Glass

My old friend, Mrs Hurst, used to take expert colour photos in the days when a good exposure meter was needed to do so. 'What meter do you use?' I asked. 'I don't use any', she replied, 'I just see how much I have to screw up my eyes'. When in the tropical sunlight, I too used to 'screw up my eyes' – until my occulist told me that I was damaging my retinas. 'Screwing up your eyes doesn't keep out the u.v. rays', he said. 'In future you must always use dark glasses.' Frequently changing over one's glasses is a nuisance, so glasses that change their darkness according to changes in the light are a boon. But how do they work?

When I found the answer to this question, I was amazed to learn that the cause of the darkening is the same as that blackening a photographic film exposed to light – not so amazing, however, as that the reverse change occurs when the glasses 'lighten' again.

The film (and the Reactolite glass) contains Ag^+ (silver ions from silver bromide). Light activates these so that they are reduced to silver and the glass darkens. But what happens in the Reactolite glass when it is removed from bright light and becomes 'light' again? This mystery was kindly solved for me by Dr Kyle of Messrs Pilkington who sent me the following explanation:-

'The reaction that converts the silver ions (Ag^+) to neutral atoms of silver (Ag) is reversible. Light energy causes the darkening reaction ($Ag^+ \rightarrow Ag$), whereas the reverse reaction (Ag Ag^+) is facilitated by infra-red rays and X-rays. The reactions occurring in the glass are greatly enhanced by traces of copper ions (Cu^+). The total reaction can be represented thus:

$$\text{darkening by light energy}$$

$$Ag^+ + Cu^+ \xrightarrow{\hspace{6cm}} Ag + Cu^{++}$$

$$\xleftarrow{\hspace{6cm}}$$

$$\text{lightening by heat energy}$$

'As all the elements involved are prisoners in the glassy matrix, they return to their original state when the source of activation is removed. There are, however, many additional complications in manufacturing these glasses to the required darkening and colour. The use of silver bromide favours brown hues whilst the use of silver chloride favours grey colours. Again, in making spectacle lenses, the glass has to be subjected to special heat treatments as it cools from its molten state.'

So although the reactions taking place in Reactolite glass are similar to those in a photographic film, they have been modified and adapted by research chemists. This was only possible through a detailed understanding of the reactions, and is a good example of the contribution of research chemists to an important aspect of modern life. I say 'important' because I used to screw up my eyes – like Mrs Hurst – when in the bright tropical sun and have damaged the retina of my left eye.

> You may think you can cope with the sun
> Wear dark glasses only for fun,
> But the sun's UV rays
> Have nasty old ways
> Causing damage to eyes to be done.

G.V.P.

CHAPTER 12: GOLD

How I became interested in metallurgy

> Near Georgetown, Colorado, is a region of enormous
> mineral wealth. There was mining everywhere. Up along
> seemingly inaccessible heights were holes with their
> roofs log-supported in which solitary men were selling
> their lives for treasure.
>
> (Isabella Bird:
> *A Lady's Life in the Rocky Mountains* (1870))

A S WE FLEW INTO JOHANNESBURG, large patches of a
yellow colour dominated the scene below. These were
waste heaps of the material remaining after the gold had
been extracted. I learnt later that it takes an average of 70
tons of rock to produce a pound's weight of gold, so there
was plenty of stuff left over (*photograph*). A few years later,
these dumps were worked over again to extract uranium
ores for use in nuclear power generation.

In 1955 the mining giant, Anglo-American Corporation
of South Africa, invited a group of 20 headmasters and
careers masters to go on a tour of their mining operations
in South Africa and Rhodesia (*photograph*). The object was
to interest them in careers in Mining Engineering. My
headmaster could not go and asked me, as his careers

master, to go in his place. I was very fortunate to be included on this prestigious tour. I became very interested in the chemical processes used in extracting metals from their ores, and the experience made my teaching of chemistry more realistic.

The tour started with a dinner in Johannesburg presided over by the Deputy Chairman, standing in for Sir Harry Oppenheimer. I remember his striking opening remarks: 'Our primary object is to make money and then to spend it for the good of all the peoples of South Africa'.

Our first visit was to the deepest gold mine in South Africa, about 9,000ft deep at that time (*photograph*). The journey down in the lift was frightening and the heat at the bottom oppressive. Returning to the surface, we saw the various processes of refining the metal. Gold is one of only a few metals that are found 'native' in the earth's crust, i.e. not combined with anything else. Even so, chemical processes have to be used to extract it from the crushed ore, using a cyanide solution. It was a bit eerie to cross a catwalk alongside a very large vat of the greenish-yellow cyanide solution (*photograph*). However, there were no records of anyone falling in. The most spectacular sight comes at the end of the process, when the molten gold is poured into a mould about the size of a building brick and the brilliant ingot of the precious metal, when cool, is removed and exposed to view – too heavy to be picked up with one hand or even two. I was told that if I could pick it up I could keep it (*photograph*).

A few years later (1960) I saw a very different sort of gold mine (*photograph*). Compared with the mines in South Africa, this was a very small and primitive operation. It was in Sarawak near a jungle village called Bau. I was on a tour sponsored by the British Council, and after visiting a number of schools to see their science teaching, I was taken to see the gold mining. Bau is about 20 miles from the capital, Kuching, and was approached by quite a good tarmac road through the jungle. Up from the road we followed a gently sloping path between tree-covered boulders into the caves where the gold-bearing rocks were being quarried. They were then taken down to an open area, where they were closely guarded in wooden sheds with padlocked doors, a security device that was hardly up to modern standards! Here the gold was extracted and purified. In 1998 I visited Bau again. The mining had ceased. The area was crudely fenced off and the jungle was invading the whole site. The wooden factory sheds had disappeared altogether. When back in Kuching, I bought a ring made of Bau gold. A few years later I was gardening and, unwisely, failed to take off the ring. Somehow or other I lost it. I hired a metal detector and it detected some rusty iron nails and an aluminium milk bottle top, but sadly not the ring. I can only think it was spotted in the sun and carried off by a raven – as folklore relates that they do.

I will now recount an episode concerning gold, the truth of which you would be justified in doubting! However, I assure you that every detail is factual and I still have the evidence that emerged.

In about 1980, when I was a lecturer at the University in Penang, I used to relax on a beach next to the Swimming Club. It was a nice sandy beach, about ½ a kilometre in length and usually almost deserted. One afternoon I was lying doing nothing when I noticed three Indian boys digging with their fingers in the sand. They were looking for some shellfish called 'siput'. These are sometimes found about 10cm below the surface and are quite good to eat after being gently fried in oil. As I lay there, I thought I might as well explore the sand myself and idly pushed my fingers down a few inches in several places. I found no siput. Then my fingers touched something hard, so I excavated a bit more and, to my amazement, brought out a gold ring. It had a purple gem mounted on it, about 3mm in diameter, which I thought was an amethyst. After washing it I walked to the Swimming Club and had my desultory swim in the pool. I then drove into town and took the ring to a jeweller. He identified the gem as alexandrite (not amethyst) and the gold as 9 carat gold – a hard alloy of gold with copper, the type used by Indian jewellers. He pointed out that both the gold and the jewel had been slightly roughened by the action of the sand and sea water. The ring was too small for me to wear (maybe it had belonged to some Indian maiden) and was no compensation for the ring of Bau gold that I had lost.

I reckoned that the chances of finding a ring in the sand where I did on that particular afternoon were less than one in a million, but if you don't believe the story, you should visit me in my home in Crawley where I keep it, and see it for yourself.

The quality of gold is expressed in 'carats' – pure gold is 24 carat, 18 carat is 75% gold. The word is derived from carob (Arabic), seed of the locust-bean plant. Apparently these seeds are consistent in their weight. One marck (a coin used by Arab traders) is said to have weighed 24 carats. It implies that the coins were made of pure gold, which is unlikely because they would then have been a bit soft. Beans are still used for weighing small objects in parts of India (and maybe elsewhere). A friend of mine from Kerala, South India, told me that when she was a girl, she saw seeds used to weigh golden objects. She showed me a large dish of the brilliant scarlet seeds which she kept as an ornament. The village goldsmith would come to the house bringing a small pair of scales with pans less than 2 inches in diameter. As weights, he used special seeds called 'kunnikuru'. They were spherical and about 1/10th inch in diameter. They were obtained from the pods of a large tree and were used to check the weights of ornaments before and after repair.

It is interesting to note that when the word 'carat' is used in connection with diamonds, it does not concern their quality, as with gold, but is a measure of their weight.

While gazing at that most impressive statue of the 'Reclining Buddha' in a Thai temple in Penang, I began to think of the immense quantities of gold that must have been used for coating it, and not only that Buddha but also the innumerable statues of emperors and gods throughout the world. From the earliest civilisations, gold leaf has been used for decorative purposes, ranging from ancient statues to modern picture frames. Those who have used gold leaf will know that it can be bought in extremely thin films (about 0.03mm thin) and that it only has to come into contact with a clean surface to stick to it for ever. I thought it would be interesting to calculate how much gold would have been needed to cover the statue of the Reclining Buddha. I allowed for four layers of gold leaf (or about 0.1 mm thickness of gold paint) and guessed that the area of the statue (which is 33 metres long) is about 250 square metres. If my calculations are correct, it seems that the amount of gold needed would have weighed about as much as the brick-sized ingot described earlier in this chapter.

My silversmith friend tells me that gold can be beaten down to this 0.03 mm by hand, but that even thinner leaf can be made by sandwiching these leaves between parchment layers and hammering them further. In this way, gold leaf only 0.0001 mm thin can be made. This leaf is transparent and is a deep green colour when you look through it.

Before he became a silversmith, my friend was a professor in the Dental School at Guy's Hospital and he told me about the old days when gold was used for some tooth fillings. It was applied in layers, each layer being hammered home – a process not popular with the patient! A later method was to use a gold amalgam, but it too is no longer used. Gold amalgam was also used in making 'silver gilt'. The amalgam consisted of a smooth paste which was easy to spread over the silver. This was then heated to drive off the mercury to leave a gold layer on the silver, a most dangerous process, no doubt resulting in a number of headaches – or even deaths. Gold plating is now done by electrolysis.

How I became interested in Metallurgy

When I was working as a Scientific Officer in the Admiralty Department of Scientific Research in 1944, a colleague named Stan Taylor was suddenly transferred to another Department. The same day he should have been at a meeting of the Admiralty Metallurgical Advisory Committee, of which he was Secretary. I suppose I must have been the only person in the Department who had some experience of metals and I was sent to take Taylor's place. I had no special knowledge of metallurgy, but that didn't matter much because the committee consisted of about 10 of the most eminent metallurgists in the country. I just had to keep the minutes of the meeting and write them up and circulate them afterwards.

The Chairman was Dr Harold Moore, Director of the British Non-Ferrous Metals Research Association and a very wise and charming elderly man. On the first two occasions he sent my minutes back – corrected as if they were school essays. This was useful training for me. We later became good friends and after he retired, he often asked me to tea at the Athenaeum Club in London. Members of the Athenaeum are mostly distinguished academics, MPs and Civil Servants and it was a great privilege to be invited as a guest. A stately curved red-carpeted stairway led from the entrance hall up to the lounges on the first floor. Dr Moore always sat in a leather-upholstered chair in a book-lined room and was served with tea, toasted tea-cakes and cherry cake by a dignified waitress of uncertain age. He always ordered two pots of tea – one of Indian and the other of China tea, so that his guest had a choice. He liked to ask me about Christ's Hospital because he was fond of the writings of Charles Lamb, the 18th century poet. Both Lamb and Samuel Taylor Coleridge had been pupils at the school at the same time.

At some meetings of the Metallurgical Committee Dr Moore's meticulousness led to arguments with other members. I remember one occasion in particular when Mr Pritchard, from Birmingham, arrived half an hour late, looking slightly flushed – no doubt after a good lunch. Towards the end of the meeting it became clear that we should not get through the agenda before Dr Moore had to leave to catch his train home. He suggested a date for the next meeting. Mr Pritchard said: 'Let's finish it today – we're used to working late in the Midlands'. To which Dr Moore bitingly replied: 'We're used to starting punctually in the south'.

I wanted to learn more about metallurgy so had lessons from Dr Ruddock, Professor of Metallurgy at the Royal Naval College, Greenwich. He gave me a lesson every Monday and afterwards took me to lunch in the famous Painted Hall, where generations of naval cadets had dined. The walls of the Hall are hung with large paintings of famous characters from naval history.

As a result of these visits I not only acquired some knowledge of metallurgy but was given some polished sections of steels and brasses as used for examination through a metallurgical microscope. These were of great use when I returned to Christ's Hospital, and formed the basis of my lessons on metallurgy. The subject was sandwiched into more orthodox, examinable parts of the chemistry syllabus. I shudder to think of what would happen if a teacher had done that sort of thing these days! Up would go the hands: 'It's not in the syllabus, Sir'. Maybe schools don't produce many metallurgists now.

As a consequence (I have always assumed), several of

my sixth form students chose to study metallurgy, and when I later visited the new Department of Metallurgy in Oxford, I found that out of only twelve undergraduates, four were old pupils of mine. Three later became Professors of Metallurgy; one became Vice-Chancellor of his university and one became the only pupil I have had who was elected a Fellow of the Royal Society.

CHAPTER 13: COPPER

From Aphrodite's mirror to Faraday's dynamo

A S I SAT ON A QUIET BEACH on the north coast of Cyprus, gazing at the brown hills in the distance, my mind wandered. 'Where are those blue remembered hills?' (A.E. Housman). Or, as the American Western says, 'There's gold in them there hills'. No, there is no gold – but there was, and still is, copper; not of course veins of metallic copper, but massive deposits of the chemical compound of copper, often with sulphur, from which the metal is obtained.

Was copper named after Cyprus or Cyprus after copper (cuprum)? 'Copper', says the *Playbook of Metals* (J.H. Pepper, 1862), 'was so called from the Isle of Cyprus, where it was first gotten in great plenty'. Earlier, Pliny the Elder (Book 24, Chapter 2) says, in BC 975: 'In Cyprus perfect copper was invented'. The Phoenicians traded cargoes from the Lebanon to Cyprus in return for the Island's 'plentiful supply of copper'. The Greeks and Romans obtained copper from Cyprus, calling it cyprium or cuprum. Anyone who has been to Cyprus will have seen road signs to the Pools of Aphrodite, the Greek Goddess of Love. She became the Roman goddess Venus. I wonder if she knew that her bright hand mirror was to become the alchemist's symbol for the metal copper.

The brown coloured 'copper hills' attracted me and we drove up and over them past the border post between Greek and Turkish Cyprus. There were still 'adits' into the underground workings and there was talk of opening up parts of the old mines again. Some of the ore may have been of 'native copper', i.e. the metal itself, but this is rare, and so to produce the metal copper, the Cypriots would have had to roast the ore with charcoal. Chemically, this is a process of reduction and involves removal of the sulphurous part of the ore, leaving the metal copper.

I did not venture into the mine workings, but some years earlier, on a visit to African mines, I was fortunate enough to be taken to the 'Copper Belt' in what was then Northern Rhodesia and is now Zambia. As we arrived at the large mine of Nchanga, I noticed a fleet of Mercedes saloon cars lined up in the car park. I thought they belonged to other visitors, but in fact they were the cars of the European miners. These were 'day-pay' men who, because of the high price of copper at the time (the 1950's), earned as much as the General Manager of the mine.

When below ground, walking along a tunnel in the Nchanga mine, I had a strange feeling of elation: I thought that there, among the brownish orange dust and rocks, lay the start of all that is made of copper – wires, cables, dynamos, motors, copper pots, brass fittings and so on. I thought of what the British scientist, Michael Faraday, had made possible through the discovery of electro-magnetism and its application to the invention of the dynamo and electric motor, and of whether he could have made his discoveries had it not been for copper. It was here that it all began. For me, it was a moment of awe that I have never forgotten.

In a deep copper mine dug by man,
Surrounded by rocks, black and tan,
I thought for a mo'
Of the old dynamo
And said 'This is where it began'.

G.V.P.

Next in the tour, we saw the plant where pure sheets of copper were obtained from slabs of the crude metal by electrolysis (*photograph*). I was used to electrolysing copper sulphate solutions in the school laboratories, when thin deposits of the bright copper resulted, but the electrolysis cells in this industrial plant were giants by comparison – hundreds of cells, about 3ft high, were joined in large zones and produced great sheets of shining metallic copper about 10ft square. The blue colour of the copper sulphate solution combined with that of the shiny copper sheets to produce a colourful scene never to be forgotten.

Ores of copper are found in many parts of the world, including Devon and Cornwall, whose mines date back many centuries but are now closed down. There are interesting stories about them. The water that flows from some copper mines contains a considerable amount of copper sulphate. It was sometimes collected in ponds and old battered iron pots and kettles, iron shavings – in fact any waste iron – was thrown into the pond. The usual change of places occurs – the iron is dissolved and the copper is precipitated. Another unusual example of the same phenomenon occurred during the early days of the Atlantic cable: the iron wires in certain places were found to be eaten away and coated with metallic copper, having probably rested on copper ore, of which there are veins in Trinity Bay.

The precipitation of copper by iron (see *Glossary*) has often been used to extract copper from sources where the content is low. The Romans used to place scrap iron in streams containing copper and over a period of months, copper was precipitated around the iron. This method was used in Hungary in the 18th century in an area including copper-rich springs and in 1750 as much as 200 tons of copper were obtained in the year. Unknown to these old-time practitioners, these processes were being helped by the activities of certain bacteria – *thiobacillus ferrooxidans*. These organisms are remarkable in many respects, e.g. they can carry out a process resembling photosynthesis and 'fix' carbon dioxide from the air by using energy derived from the oxidation of iron (II) (Fe^{2+} Fe^{3+}) and from the oxidation of sulphur. During the past 50 years huge dumps of low grade copper ore, containing less than ½% of copper, have been treated by T. ferrooxidans and sulphuric acid. The process is slow and inefficient but can increase the copper content of the dumps to above 1% (David Holmes, *Chemistry and Industry*, 4.1.99).

White Brass

Brass and bronze are of course the commonest alloys of copper. Brass is an alloy of copper with zinc and bronze an alloy of copper with tin and other metals such as manganese. But I have no special events to relate concerning them, so will tell you about White Brass, about which I got to know enough to publish a paper in the *Journal of Historical Metallurgy* in 1979.

While attending a small party in the house of the Vice Chancellor of the University in Penang, where I was a lecturer, I noticed some fine polished stand-dishes, about 10–12 inches in diameter, that looked very like silver. They could have been silver or stainless steel or local pewter (95% tin). Yet they didn't look quite like any of these. I asked the Vice Chancellor what they were. 'They are dishes used in traditional Malay wedding ceremonies. They are made in a village industry on the east coat of Malaysia', he told me. 'What are they made of?', I asked. 'They're tembaga puteh.' I wasn't much the wiser, as this meant 'white metal'. I asked what that was, but the only answer I got was: 'I don't know. You had better go to Trengganu and find out.'

First I went to the University library and found that a British administrator, R Winstedt, had visited Trengganu almost a century ago and reported on a village industry that was making articles in white brass. He described the process and wrote that the craftsmen had learnt the details from 'an artisan from Linga'. This is an island not far from Singapore and the Sultan of Linga had sent this artisan to Trengganu at the request of their Sultan, to whom he was related.

To cast objects in white brass the old 'lost wax' process was still used. A model is made in wax, then coated with a paste made from rice husks and placed in a hot oven. The wax runs out, leaving a mould which is then filled with the molten metal. On cooling, the mould is removed to leave a perfect replica of the original wax model. Winstedt only used the words 'tembaga puteh' for the metal. So I set off to Trengganu to find out what it was.

After exploring a section of the coastal area, I found the small factory beneath coconut trees in a clearing off a path leading away from the town. A number of Malay men were busy working on various jobs, and were very willing to show me the whole process of making white brass. Shelves of brass objects, mostly stand-trays, rice husk moulds and boxes of a mixture of metals were lying around. At last I was near to finding out what 'tembaga puteh' was made from. The boxes contained old cartridge cases made of ordinary brass, some thick wires of lead and some rods of a white metal which they told me consisted of an alloy of nickel and zinc. I was very surprised to hear that nickel was used, as this is a high melting point metal, only isolated from its ore in 1751 and not available in quantity until after the year 1898. Yet one Malay man working at the plant gave me the names of four generations of his relatives who had been working there. His great-grandfather must have been working there before 1900.

The Malay brass makers said that white brass was made by melting together 4 parts of ordinary brass, 2½ parts of nickel, 1 part of zinc and a little lead. After my visit I had two samples of white brass analysed. One was an antique stand-tray bought at a scrap market in Rope Walk, Penang. The other was a stand-tray such as is sold today in Trengganu. Both looked silvery when polished. The old one remained that way for many years but the modern one tarnished easily and looked like ordinary brass in a few weeks. The analysis showed that the latter contained 3.2% of nickel where the old one contained 9.6%. Nickel is expensive, so the craftsmen were now economising and using less – to the detriment of the product.

History of White Brass

I read in the remarkable twelve-volume *Science and Civilisation in China* by Joseph Needham that the Chinese were making alloys of copper and nickel as far back as the 1st century AD. The alloy was called Pak Fong and was used for coinage, as first mentioned in 420 AD. Its use became more frequent after the 12th century. A method was developed for making it that strongly resembled alchemy – it was described by Ho Wei about 1095 AD. First, ordinary brass was melted in a crucible. An 'earth' was then thrown in, causing white fumes and a choking gas to be emitted while the brass turned to silver! The 'earth' was probably an ore of nickel with arsenic and sulphur. The white fumes would be arsenious oxide and the choking gas sulphur dioxide. The nickel would be released directly into the brass, forming nickel brass, without ever being freed as the elemental metal. This was not isolated until 1751, so it is interesting that the Chinese were able to make its alloy, 'white brass', many centuries before nickel itself was available.

The nickel ore used in this old process came from the mountainous region of Yunnan in southern China. I was interested to find that the Chinese people who emigrated to northern Malaysia added Yunnani after their names.

This made me wonder whether they were responsible for introducing this method of making white brass to the people of Trengganu. But I could find no evidence for this. If it had happened, there would have later been a fundamental change in the method, for the Chinese started with nickel ores and the Malays started with nickel. I even wondered whether the 'secret' brought to Trengganu by the artisan from Linga was how white brass could be made directly from the metal. But this is entirely speculation.

It was first realised that Pak Fong contained nickel in 1778 and in about 1820 imitations were made in Berlin and were referred to as 'German silver', an alloy much used in coinage.

Objects made of the Chinese alloy were shipped to England by the East India Company and there is a note in the Public Records Office in London for the year 1760 referring to 'white copper'. This was most commonly used for making candlesticks and fire-irons and I noticed that the fire-irons displayed around a fireplace in Knole Castle, Sevenoaks appeared to be made of Pak Fong. Records exist of the analysis of many candlesticks made from the Chinese alloy during the 18th century. The nickel content varied from 10 to 20%(The average nickel content in German silver is about 15%.)

The production of nickel metal expanded when its use for nickel plating was adopted. In 1890 the Mond Nickel Company started production in Sudbury, Canada and remains the world's largest producer of nickel. It is probably from there (via Singapore) that the nickel alloy came which is now used by the Malays in Trengganu.

Years ago the Chinese made Pak Fong,
Producing a terrible pong.
But the modern Malays
Use different ways
Which are clean – and do not take so long.

G.V.P.

CHAPTER 14: DIAMOND

Surprisingly enough, diamonds are crystals of soot.

Mary had a little lamb
Its coat was black as soot
And everywhere that Mary went
Its sooty foot it put.

I ONCE VISITED THE DIAMOND MINES at Pretoria and Kimberley in South Africa. The diamond crystals there grew in 'pipes' of volcanic rock when it was still liquid at great depth in the earth. The pipes are mined from the top downwards, leaving big holes in the landscape (*photograph*). The most striking features of the surroundings were the vast heaps of waste rock stretching away into the distance. These consisted of crushed rock known as 'tailings', left over when the diamond crystals had been removed. In order to extract 1lb weight of diamonds, over 11,000 tons of rock has to be crushed. Hence the great quantity of waste.

The upper parts of the pipes are exposed to weathering and over the centuries in certain localities the diamonds in them are washed out and transported by streams into rivers, eventually being deposited along the shores of the sea. So if you take a walk along the 'Diamond Coast' in

South West Africa you may find a diamond – if you're lucky.

During our visit we were taken to the laboratories where the newly extracted crystals were sorted. Most of them were small octagonal pyramids about ½cm across and of a dirty pale yellowish-brown colour. They were laid out in piles on sheets of white paper on a flat bench. While we were there, one of our party put his hot, moist forearm on to the paper to have a closer look. As he lifted his arm again paper and diamonds were scattered on the floor. 'Never mind', said our guide, 'they are uncut and not worth much', and he swept them up with a dustpan and brush. They only become valuable when cut into gem-stones and we were shown a fine collection of such cut stones, mostly colourless but a few faintly coloured pink, blue and yellow. When considering a gemstone, one should look for the 'four C's' – cut, clarity, colour and carats.

We were told the story of how the famous Cullinan diamond was shipped to England in the last century. A special package was made with two layers of protective material, firmly sealed and sent by courier. But the dia-mond was not in it – this was sent in an ordinary parcel and arrived safely. True? I wonder!

I have been interested in the growth of crystals for many years and the mine owners, de Beers, kindly lent me three crystals of diamond to study in the laboratory when I got home. I was also able to borrow about twenty diamond crystals from the Mineralogical Department of the Natural History Museum in London. These crystals were all 'in situ', i.e. still attached to the rock in which they had been formed. Some were from South Africa, some from the Belgian Congo and others from Brazil.

In order to find out more about how the crystals had grown, I studied their surfaces through the microscope. As with other crystals, they grew as added material spread over the existing surfaces as 'growth sheets'. It looked as if the new material had started to deposit at a few points on the crystal surface and spread out over the surface until it was covered. New growth sheets started to spread out before the previous sheets had finished spreading, so the series of sheets formed growth 'hillocks'. These often formed complex patterns over the crystal surface. These patterns must be related to the circumstances in which the crystals had grown and attempts have been made to deduce information from the patterns about the temperatures and rates of growth of the diamonds.

Several attempts to grow crystals of diamond were made in the 19th century. Probably the best known were those of a Scottish inventor, James B Hannay. In his experiments, he sealed up fish-oil with the soft metal lithium in a gun barrel and heated it in a furnace placed in the middle of a field for safety. He hoped that the lithium, which has a strong affinity for hydrogen, would react with the hydrocarbons in the fish-oil and release the carbon in the form of diamond. One day, after many failures (in one of which the gun-barrel exploded and killed one of the workmen), he thought he had succeeded. Eleven small hard grains were found in the barrel when it was opened. These were identified by the Keeper of the Minerals at the British Museum, Sir Jasper Maskelyne, as diamonds. The use of X-rays to identify crystals had not been developed by then and Hannay's claim was disputed by other scientists.

However, during World War II, when the Museum was removing its precious possessions to safer places, a small box was found labelled 'Hannay's Diamonds'. The then Keeper of the Minerals, Dr A Bannister, who was an X-ray crystallographer, had the crystals examined by X-rays and found that they had the structure of diamond.

Industrial diamonds were made synthetically from about 1950, but to produce them, extremely high pressures and temperatures, unlikely to have been achieved in Hannay's gun-barrel, are needed. So there is still a mystery surrounding Hannay's diamonds. It has been suggested that some of his workmen put the diamonds in the gun-barrel beforehand, hoping that 'success' would stop any more experiments of the sort that killed a colleague. How suspicious can one be?

The quality of synthetic diamonds has improved to such an extent that they compete with the natural diamonds marketed by de Beers. At first, de Beers were able to detect under a microscope tiny traces of aluminium in the synthetic diamonds, but the scientists learnt how to prevent this. Laboratory diamonds were, however, always detectable because of their yellow colour, due to trapped nitrogen. Scientists then managed to disperse the nitrogen and produce clear diamonds. Then the de Beers' team discovered under ultra-violet light that the structure of a manufactured diamond is composed of the normal octrahedra of carbon atoms but also some telltale little cubes not found in natural diamonds. An industrious team of Russian scientists, backed by American money, claims to have eliminated the cubes. De Beers have taken to stamping natural diamonds to authenticate them. Where will the struggle end?

The latest development in the sphere of synthetic diamonds is the development of a process in which thin films of diamond can be deposited on a substrate or flat surface. This is achieved by using an extremely high temperature – several thousand degrees – and injecting into the containing plasma a simple compound of carbon – methane. The molecule of methane consists of four hydrogen atoms joined to a single carbon atom. These molecules are completely shattered at these high temperatures and free atoms swill around in the resulting 'soup'. Some of these hit the substrate and link together, forming the characteristic tetrahedral structure of diamond.

These thin sheets of synthetic diamond have all the characteristic properties of diamond – extreme hardness, good electrical insulation etc. They can also be 'doped' with small quantities of other elements and made into semi-conductors such as are used in many types of electronic equipment. Such developments will depend on the possibility of finding a substrate that will withstand the high temperatures needed to make the diamond films. The temperature of the substrate may reach 900°C, and at present silicon is used. By achieving a lower temperature at which to split up the methane, it may be possible to use more versatile substrates, such as glass. Because of the way it is made, this form of diamond is known as CVD – chemical vapour deposition.

Carbon is a remarkable element. Not only can its atoms join together in little groups, as in soot, but they can also form carbon fibres, graphite and diamond, by joining up to make different patterns.

In diamond, each carbon atom is joined to four others in a three-dimensional pattern. This symmetrical arrangement results in an extremely hard solid, diamond, the hardest substance found in nature. By contrast, graphite is quite soft. On Moh's scale of hardness, diamond is 10 and graphite is 1 – 2. The structure of graphite consists of layers of hexagons of carbon atoms in a plane, each atom being joined to three others. The planes of hexagons are grouped in a pile one above the other, each plane being joined to the next one by rather weak forces. This is why the planes slip easily over each other and explains why graphite is a good lubricant.

Carbon in the form of graphite has long been used in gas masks to adsorb poisonous gases and enable the residual air to be inhaled. This property of graphite is also used on a large scale to remove noxious gases from the air in chemical factories. The ability of activated carbon to absorb large quantities of vapour has been known for centuries – in 1600 BC the Egyptians used charcoal for medical purposes, e.g. reduction of 'wind'. In some experiments I was doing I once tried to 'de-gas' some carbon. I heated it in a vacuum and measured the amount of water vapour that came off. When no more came, I raised the temperature and more water vapour was evolved. I then raised the temperature of the carbon again until no more vapour came off. This did not happen until over 1200°C – showing how very strongly carbon holds on to the vapour it has adsorbed.

Research scientists have now been able to produce forms

of carbon that do not occur in nature. One well-known example is carbon fibre, in which the atoms are arranged in long rows firmly attached to each other, providing very strong fibres that can be used for reinforcing other materials such as ceramics, plastics and even metals.

A more recent discovery is a form of carbon called buckminster-fullerene, in which the atoms are arranged in a spherical open network, each group containing 60 atoms, familiarly known as 'Bucky Balls'. This has special uses in industrial chemistry, e.g. in separating similar compounds from each other by acting as a kind of molecular sieve.

One wonders how the scientists came to make these new stuffs. Maybe their thoughts moved from diamonds, where the bonding between the atoms is very strong and symmetrical in three dimensions, through graphite, where the strong bonding is confined to two dimensions, to the thought that if stuff could be made where the strong bonds were only in one dimension, fibres would be formed – carbon fibres. These would be strong in the dimension of their length, but weak in other dimensions, so that the fibres would be flexible – and suitable for making the frames of tennis rackets and golf clubs. But how could such a form of carbon be manufactured?

In about 1960 a fine black, silky filament of pure carbon was produced by heat treatment of a certain plastic fibre. This fibre was obtained from acrylonitrite, $CH_2. CH. CN$, by causing the molecules to join together in long chains called, of course, 'polyacrylonitrite'. This carbon fibre is used for re-inforcing plastics, producing a composite that is very stiff and four times as strong as high tensile steel. It has been used not only for making the frames of tennis rackets and fishing rods, but also in the manufacture of parts for motor cars, aircraft, space structures and in other civil engineering applications.

So to what structure and bonding between the carbon atoms does carbon fibre owe its strength? One important point is that the crystal structure must be uniform and uninterrupted by impurities or dislocations which would weaken it. The fact that the fibres are used enclosed in plastic protects them from surface damage, but inside these protective layers, each carbon atom is joined to four other atoms in the tetrahedral structure that is characteristic of diamond crystal. This structure owes its strength to that of the carbon – carbon bonds. So one might say, as suggested above, that the carbon fibres are uni-directional diamond crystals, but that would be stretching it a bit (although 'stretching' is the last kind of deformation one could do to a diamond crystal!)

Recent research has resulted in the formation of minute structures of carbon atoms of the same dimensions as 'Bucky balls' but in the form of tubes. It is hoped that these will store hydrogen for use in engines fuelled by this gas. The principle is as follows: The ability of carbon granules to adsorb gases, as a sponge soaks up water, is well known. The bigger the molecules of the gas, the greater is the tendency of carbon to adsorb them, but molecules as small as those of water vapour or even hydrogen can also be adsorbed.

The present interest in this phenomenon centres around the ability of carbon to adsorb hydrogen – a very small molecule (H_2). A special form of carbon in which the atoms are joined up to make minute grids has been made. These forms consist of minute tubes, called nanotubes, and minute fibres called nano fibres. They are said to absorb so much hydrogen that it would be possible to make an assembly carrying enough hydrogen to work fuel cells which could power a small car for several hundred miles.

Carbon Chemistry

Carbon atoms, in addition to joining up with themselves in these several different ways, combine with other elements to make literally millions of compounds. For this reason, the study of carbon compounds makes up a whole section of chemistry called Organic Chemistry – because many of the compounds are formed in nature and it was originally thought that some 'vital force' was concerned in their production. Many organic compounds consist only of carbon and hydrogen and are called 'hydrocarbons'. A great number of hydrocarbons constitute natural gas and petroleum. Many other organic compounds also contain oxygen, and these are called 'carbohydrates'. Examples are sugar, starch and cellulose. The number of compounds containing carbon becomes even greater when they also contain nitrogen, as in proteins. There are organic compounds that also contain metals such as iron, magnesium, potassium. Haemoglobin contains iron and a similar compound in green plants, chlorophyll, has magnesium instead of iron. In his chapter on Carbon, Primo Levi, in his book *The Periodic Table*, tells a fascinating story of the life of a carbon atom as he imagines it might have been. The story goes something like this:

Starting as part of a limestone cliff, a carbon atom finds

itself in a lime kiln and launched into the air as a carbon dioxide molecule. Blown over Italy, it lands on a vine leaf and is absorbed during photosynthesis, becoming part of a molecule, with five other carbon atoms, as glucose. It enjoys the wine-making process of fermentation and, as alcohol, it enters the liver of a wine imbiber. It stays there for some time but after a week is carried by the blood stream into a muscle fibre. Another change, and it is part of lactic acid and providing energy for its host. It is released once again in a carbon dioxide molecule. Blown hither and thither it finishes up over Lebanon and is absorbed by the leaf of a cedar tree. Gobbled by a wood worm and passing into its pupa, it is liberated again in part of the eye of an ugly, grey moth. Death and decay overtake the moth but the carbon atom is freed as carbon dioxide to be blown around once more in the atmosphere. According to Levi, it will spend an average of 200 years there before it again becomes 'fixed' in some material such as limestone. It would be too late to take part in building up a diamond!

> Scintillate, scintillate, globule vivific
> Feign would I fathom your nature specific
> Perched up above in the ether capacious
> Strongly resembling a jewel carbonaceous.

> (After *Twinkle, Twinkle Little Star*)
> Anon.

CHAPTER 15: MEDICINES

Traditional remedies and new drugs

Traditional Medicine

FROM TIME IMMEMORIAL man has used various natural products to treat ill health. So many traditional medicines continue to be used that there is surely some truth in what is claimed for them. Maybe auto-suggestion is sometimes a factor, but I find it difficult to believe that the action of extract of senna pods, in relieving constipation, is entirely due to the imagination. The list of 'natural remedies' is endless – quinine, as extracted from the bark of cinchona trees, has been too effective as an anti-malarial drug to be ignored. So much so that synthetic quinine has been used in its place and it has given rise to research which has produced stuff that is superior in its action and usefulness.

'An apple a day keeps the doctor away' – maybe the reasons have not always been known, but now we give the credit to the vitamins and fibres in the good old apple! And what about rhubarb for constipation and St John's Wort, popular in Europe for centuries? Eskimos survive on codliver oil and we give it to our children and old people as a source of vitamins A and D. It also lowers the cholesterol level and the risk of heart trouble. Try mint chicory for the digestion – our ancestors have used this for centuries. I must confess to a weakness for milk thistle. You won't see me among the donkeys in a field chewing the prickly thistle but I take an extract when I get 'heartburn' after eating fried food for supper. It is alleged to improve the function of the liver. All I know is that when I am 'on' sillimarin (as the extract of milk thistle is called) I get no heartburn and sleep well.

There is the temptation to take too many of these 'nature cures'. I have a Canadian friend who, when visiting me, takes a pill box out of her handbag after breakfast and consumes 14 different pills. Overdoing it a bit, I think, but she insists that her arthritis gets worse if she omits even one of them.

There is such strong faith in the efficacies of natural herbs that 'herb gardens' have been established for many years. Originally the monks planted them, then universities followed. The first botanic garden in Britain was founded in 1620 in Oxford. Basing their collections on medicinal plants, other gardens followed and today there are over 50 botanical gardens in the UK. They include many herbs that date back to the 16th and 17th centuries or even earlier. Thus valerian, a plant known for centuries, was used for 'old sores, swellings, piles, broken ruptures. It also clears the eyes and expelleth worms. It profiteth against a pestilent aire and ache of the hips'. One favourite scented plant, lily of the valley, has long been used – the flowers, when distilled with wine, 'will restore speech to those who have the dumb palsie and are fallen with apoplexy and are good against gout and comfort the heart'.

Botanic gardens were founded in Europe and through-out the world for reasons which ranged from the utilitarian to the aesthetic and they had an important educational function. Consider their role in medicine. Apothecaries took many of their remedies, 'simples' as they were called, from plants, and it was vital that their training should include some stiff tests on plant recognition. The most important garden in London was the Chelsea Physic Garden, which the Society of Apothecaries set up in 1673. The garden, like others of its kind, was a factory for established drugs, a test bed for new varieties and an important teaching resource for the Society. Apprentices visited the garden for instruction from the Demonstrator of Plants, with whom they also went 'herbalising' in the countryside.

The well known botanist, Sir Joseph Banks, who travelled with Captain Cook to Australia and New Zea-land, brought back many plants, most of which were later grown at the Chelsea garden. Early in the year 2000 I was enjoying a walk along a cliff-top path at Burrewaree in New South Wales. The views of the sea and the rocky inlets were spectacular, but the most fascinating feature was the bush around me that consisted mostly of the striking bottle-brush trees called *Banksia grandis*. Between 10 to 30 ft high, the trees bear yellow bottle-brush flowers that grow upright from the branches and look like fat candles on a Christmas tree. The *Banksia* include some 50 species of trees and shrubs, and were named after Sir Joseph Banks.

In 1773 Banks became Director of the Royal Gardens at Kew, and in 1778 he was appointed President of the Royal Society, a position he retained until his death in 1820. His vision of Kew was of a vast plant exchange at the centre of an array of botanic gardens throughout the world. Men who had spent time at Kew went out to cultivate the plants of several continents and to found botanic gardens in their turn in India, the West Indies, Africa and the Far East.

Plants are still important as sources of medicines. At one point it was found that twelve out of the twenty-five top-earning drugs were derived from natural products. In the developing world it is estimated that 80% of medicines prescribed are from plants. Indian scientists and ecologists are now worried about their ancient knowledge being 'pirated' by the Western world. They justifiably protested at an American patent taken out on a combination of three herbs long known in India to have anti-diabetic properties.

As might be expected, older civilisations have strong beliefs about the use of herbs as medicines. Ancient lists include products from minerals as well as animals and plants, some of which are well known, e.g. sulphur as a mild disinfectant, mercury compounds as violent purges and arsenic oxide as a fatal poison. A recent book of Chinese medicines includes more than 5,000 natural sources, of which 83% are plants. Traditional medicines from herbs whose properties have been tested over thousands of years sometimes provide the basis from which to make modern medicines. More than 500 herbs have been studied and hundreds of chemical compounds isolated. A good example is the development of the anti-malarial drug artimether or artimisinin from the plant artemesia. This compound was mentioned in old Chinese manuscripts as a treatment for fevers. The modern drug acts against the malaria parasite and is effective in places where the parasite has become resistant to quinine, the traditional anti-malarial drug.

In several other Chinese centres, biochemical techniques are being applied to the task of deriving modern medicines from traditional remedies. At the Chinese Pharmaceutical University, research workers are identifying and classifying Chinese herbs by establishing their DNA fingerprints. This will help in future research and in quality control of raw herbal material.

These modern investigations have justified the use of many traditional Chinese medicines. For example a tea made from a certain moss is a traditional drink taken by elderly people. It has now been shown to contain a chemical that has beneficial effects on the memory. Another example is provided by a tea made from ten plants listed in a traditional Chinese recipe for treating eczema. Attempts to simplify the mixture failed – all ten herbs are necessary!

My friend Tony Mansell once asked a Chinese professor, whose wife was a doctor spending a year at King's College, London, whether his wife practised Chinese traditional medicine. He said: 'Yes, for slow diseases, and Western medicine for fast ones'. For 'slow' read 'chronic' and for 'fast' 'acute', and you have a very sensible approach.

The Chinese have great faith in their traditional remedies and are often quite rigid in their beliefs about them. My friend Chuah, seeing I had painful knee joints, recommended codliver oil – 'It's good for all cases of wind'. 'But I haven't got wind – I've got arthritic joints.' 'We Chinese believe that this is due to wind in the joints.' A friend of mine finds that codliver oil 'works' for his arthritic knees.

Chinese views on food and cooking are also traditional and strictly adhered to. My Chinese visitors insist on cooking their recipes exactly as they always have done – no small changes suggested by me are acceptable! I think this strong belief is connected with the importance of the family. Family links are primary factors in their philosophy. Respect for customs in medicine and cooking is strong.

New Medicines for Old

Traditional medicines were discovered by usage – try it and see if it works. As the knowledge and skills of chemists increased, they were sometimes able to work out why and how. They could even work out the complex structures in the plants that gave them medicinal properties and could make copies in their laboratories. They could then try to alter these copies to make substances that were more effective or selective or more capable of outwitting bacteria than the original. A good example will be found below. (See under Migraine.)

Other modern medicines have been discovered by less systematic procedures. Penicillin was discovered by Sir Alexander Fleming as a result of some spores accidentally blowing in through his laboratory window on to dishes containing jelly infected with bacteria. The bacteria died. This discovery was of incalculable value. This was in 1928, but it was not until 1941 that the work of Chain and Florey made penicillin available for use as an antibiotic. This revolutionised the treatment of infection from that time on. It became widely used in preventing wounds from going septic and allowing them to heal.

The use of penicillin in World War II saved the lives of innumerable wounded soldiers, whose open wounds could be treated quickly. During World War I, in contrast, wounded soldiers were taken back from France to hospitals in England. It so happens that my father was a doctor at one of them, the Cambridge Hospital, Aldershot, and saw many cases where wounds had gone septic leading to loss of life that could have been prevented by the use of antibiotics.

The discovery of the medicine Salvarsan, which kills syphilis bacteria and is not very toxic to human beings, was more deliberate and resulted from the realisation that there is a link between the structure of the molecule of the drug and its properties. The story is this:

Salvarsan

By the end of the 19th century Germany was the centre of the world's dyestuff industry and among the many dyes synthesised by German chemists was a class known as azo dyes. The chemical reaction used for making these dyes was discovered in 1864 at a brewery in Burton-on-Trent. The dyes were molecules containing a group of nitrogen atoms -N=N-, called azo groups. (See *Glossary*)

Dyes were used to stain specimens for examination under the microscope. A young medical student, Paul Ehrlich, was fascinated by the way dyes selectively stained tissues, colouring some parts of the specimen but not all. He thought that the azo group was important in this selectivity and wondered if he could use the idea to make a molecule which would stain bacteria but not the tissue of the person infected. If the dye could be made poisonous to the bacteria, then it might be possible to use it as a drug to kill the germ without harming the person. The element nitrogen does not give rise to poisonous compounds but its close relation, arsenic, does. Ehrlich decided to make dyes in which the azo group was replaced by -As=As-. After synthesising 606 such dyes he came up with one which killed syphilis bacteria and was not toxic to people. It was called Salvarsan, or Arsphenamine and was patented in 1911. (See *Glossary*)

This was the first example of what was referred to as a 'magic bullet'. Ehrlich's realisation of the link between the structure of a molecule and its properties is still the basis for modern pharmaceutical research into the production of new drugs and the modification of existing ones to defeat resistant strains of bacteria. The use of Salvarsan provided a dramatic cure for the sexually transmitted disease of syphilis.

Aspirin

I have long had a great faith in aspirin – a 'wonder drug'. It is a good example of a medicine developed from a natural product. Oil of wintergreen has long been used to relieve painful joints and strains. It contains the substance methyl salicylate which was first made synthetically in Germany in 1885 and hence became available on a large scale. Salicylic acid, derived from it, has many beneficial effects but unfortunately is damaging to the lining of the stomach. This effect can be reduced by using one of its compounds, aspirin (see *Glossary*). Unfortunately aspirin also has side effects and can be dangerous if taken in excess. During a conference I was once attending on

Chemical Education, the Chief Inspector of Education (Chemistry), Norman Booth, woke up one night in a pool of blood. He had been taking eight aspirin tablets to try to cure his feverish cold in time for his lecture in the morning. He recovered eventually. However, this deleterious effect of aspirin can be partly avoided by the use of dispersable (partly soluble) aspirin, which does not settle down on the stomach wall. Chemists make this stuff by converting the salicylic acid into its sodium salt (see *Glossary*).

Aspirin is really a wonder drug for which new uses are even now being found. For example, not only does it relieve pain, it also thins the blood when taken in small quantities and is now prescribed to prevent heart attacks and strokes and to treat them in their early stages. I take half an aspirin every day. It is a substance which can reduce body temperature and it is also used to relieve the symptoms of fever – as in flu. A big test of the effect of aspirin on sufferers from heart troubles was recently carried out in the USA. Over 10,000 patients were treated with aspirin and an equal number given a placebo (or harmless tablet). After 3 years the test had to be stopped because the patients taking aspirin were in so much better health than the others.

Aspirin is only one of a group of medicines called N.S.A.I.D. (non-steroidal anti-inflammatory drugs). All are widely prescribed for inflammatory conditions but, if used regularly, all can also cause mild or serious stomach damage. But help is at hand in the form of a chemical compound well known to all chemistry students. It is nitrogen oxide, the gas formed when the oxygen and nitrogen of the air combine in an electric arc – as in the Birkeland-Eyde Process (see 'Food – Growing It'). Nitrogen oxide is very active stuff and combines readily with many other compounds. Over the last few years it has been found to play a lively role in the human body. It is involved in the nervous system, in combating infection and in regulating blood pressure. Research workers explored the possibility of attaching NO to NSAIDs, such as aspirin, in the hope that a new type of NSAID would be produced which relieves pain but causes no gastric damage. Manufacturers have NO drugs in the pipeline which have already been shown to be good painkillers and have reduced the gastric side effects. Other NO drugs are under development for treating osteoporosis, asthma, inflammation of the bowel, Alzheimer's disease and others. More trials have to be done, but the outlook seems promising.

Migraine

When I was in my teens I used to get an occasional mild attack of migraine. I used to swallow aspirin and lie down for a couple of hours. Later in life, instead of taking the form of an intense headache, the migraine manifested itself as semi-haloes made up of lightly coloured segments that flickered across my sight. But these attacks were nothing like as severe as those suffered by my ex-colleague, Colin Healey. He was a teacher and the attacks were so severe that he just had to take a day off. When he became a headmaster, not surprisingly, they got worse. Shortly after he retired he had a slight stroke, affecting his left arm and leg. He soon recovered enough to play golf regularly. But surprise, surprise, he never had another attack of migraine. I wonder what happened to his brain structure to produce this beneficial result.

The development of a drug to help migraine is another example of where the starting point for the research chemist was a substance originally isolated from nature in its oral form – a fungus found in plants. It is called ergotamine. The remarkable work of chemists in making a medicine that will cure migraine is described in one of the booklets written for students by Glaxo Wellcome.

Glaxo Wellcome first became interested in migraine in the 1970s and had some new ideas about how it might be treated. A chemical that plays a key role in migraine is called 5-hydroxytriptamine or 5HT for short. This compound can be found in some of the cells that make up the blood, stomach, intestines and brain and plays a key role in their functions. It exerts its effects by acting at certain sites known as 5HT receptors. These are large flexible molecules situated on the surfaces of cells that have the ability to recognise and react with the 5HT molecules.

Many years ago it was discovered that the amount of 5HT in the blood fell considerably during a migraine attack and that migraine was triggered by an abnormally low level of 5HT in the bloodstream. It might therefore be thought that 5HT could be given as a medicine for migraine but, because of the side effects it can cause, this is not so.

Both ergotamine and 5HT cause the blood vessels to constrict to a small diameter, so could it be that migraine headaches were caused by the blood vessels on the surface of the brain becoming distended and that the chemicals could relieve the pain by constricting the swollen vessels? Unfortunately these chemicals are not selective and constrict the blood vessels all over the body, causing various side effects. So if a way could be found to selectively constrict only the blood vessels on the surface of the brain, a cure for migraine could be evolved. After years of research, Glaxo Wellcome biologists succeeded in doing this. The process is enormously challenging – just to make a new molecule may take 1 or 2 months, and then it has to be tested. At Glaxo Wellcome it took a team of 6 – 9 chemists about 8 years to make over 800 compounds before one was identified as being appropriate for testing on humans.

The development process took about 20 years of painstaking research and cost the company over £100 million to bring the product to the market. The scientists involved in the discovery got immense satisfaction from knowing that the new medicines could bring relief to migraine sufferers throughout the world.

The development of a new medicine for migraine is just one example of the way new drugs are sometimes made. However, it is a lengthy and expensive process and it may be possible to take some short cuts.

More new drugs from old

A substance obtained from the Calabar bean in Southern Nigeria, which was formerly used as a poison, has given rise to useful drugs. The beans contain a chemical called physostigmine which has been used in the treatment of glaucoma, a disease affecting the eyes mainly of elderly people. (The treatment has maintained the sight of my friend Ken Mappin in good order for many years.) Physostigmine has also been used as a starting-point for the design of synthetic drugs. These have included several insecticides (e.g. carbaryl) and also, recently, a drug for treating Alzheimer's. The molecule of this drug, called rivastigmine, resembles that of its parent molecule physostigmine. The only difference is in two simple groups in a complex molecule.

Another natural product that is said to have significant beneficial effects in Alzheimer's disease is gingko extract obtained from the leaves of gingko biloba, but there is no hard evidence yet. It is used in Chinese medicine for asthma and in the West for treating damage to the central nervous system.

Alzheimer's is, as you will know, a very sad disease. My sister suffered from it but the nurses in the home said she was happier than I was. A story rings true. It is of the poor old lady who was suffering from Alzheimer's whose son greeted her by asking: 'Do you know who I am?' She replied 'No, but ask the nurse – she will be able to tell you'.

Anaesthetics

Anaesthetics are one of the greatest boons which medical science has given us. Simple molecules like nitrous oxide, chloroform and ether are now supplemented by an array of chemicals which can be used for either general or local anaesthesia. If patients are to undergo surgery, they would prefer to have an anaesthetic than to follow the practices of olden times, where a tourniquet was put round the diseased limb before it was cut and molten tar applied.

Anyone who has been in hospital for surgical treatment will know they have reason to be grateful for the discovery and development of anaesthetics, but the full part played by the anaesthetist during an operation is seldom realised by the patient. An injection into a vein or the simple inhalation of a pleasant smelling gas under a face mask is all they remember. Throughout their time in the operating theatre they have been kept unconscious, free from any sensation of the surgical treatment and with their muscles in a relaxed condition to help the surgeons in their work, with the vital functions of breathing and blood circulation unaffected. This has been achieved by the skill and continuous attention of the anaesthetist and has been made possible by the discovery of modern anaesthetic agents.

When I had an operation for a knee replacement, I remember lying on the trolley outside the operating theatre and asking the nurse why we were waiting.

'What do you mean?', she said, 'Waiting for what?'

'For the operation of course', I said.

'Oh', she said, 'You've had it'!

> 'It was easy', said an old man from Spain
> 'I got my new hip without pain.
> Now to make a fresh start
> I've hopes for a heart
> But what I want most's a new brain.'

F.G.T.

Some of the older anaesthetics which have been in use over the past century or so are probably well known to you – at least as names. Nitrous oxide, formula N_2O, was discovered by Priestley (the discoverer of oxygen) in 1773, and in 1800 Humphry Davy (the discoverer of sodium, potassium and other elements) wrote about its pain-killing properties and indeed suggested its use for surgical operations. Another anaesthetic, ether, was first described by Valerius Cordus in 1540. The intoxicating effects it produced following inhalation were known for many years before the first real demonstration of its usefulness as an anaesthetic for general surgery. Its use soon became widespread in the United States and in other countries. One of the great British surgeons, Robert Liston, employed ether for the first time as an anaesthetic for the amputation of a leg in University College Hospital, London on 21st December 1846. Ether can be made from ordinary alcohol (ethanol) by the action of sulphuric acid. Ether and alcohol provide a good example of the way the molecular structure of substances influences their properties. Notice that the molecules of both ether and alcohol (see *Glossary*) contain the same number of atoms – 2 of carbon, 6 of hydrogen and 1 of oxygen, yet their arrangement in the 2 molecules is different. It is this difference that makes ether render you unconscious whereas alcohol only makes you drunk.

Chloroform, discovered by the French chemist, Dumas, in 1834, was first used as an anaesthetic by the surgeon James Young Simpson in 1847. The name 'chloroform' suggests that the molecule contains chlorine. The last syllable suggests that it is related to such compounds as the preservative formaldehyde and to formic acid, the poisonous liquid in the sting of ants. Both words are derived from the French for ant, 'fourmi'. The formulae of their molecules, from which you can see the relationship between the three substances, are given in the Glossary.

Chloroform acts more quickly than ether and was often used in conjunction with it. Other general anaesthetics are chloroethane, introduced in 1894 for the first time in Sweden and Austria, and trichloroethylene, introduced in 1934. Formerly, however, ether had been the most widely used anaesthetic in hospitals all over the world.

One of the hazards associated with the use of ether in operating theatres is the flammability and explosive property of its vapour when mixed with air or oxygen. After a number of explosions, some with fatal consequences, efforts were made to discover a non-explosive substitute for ether with similar anaesthetic properties. At that time, in the 1950s, little was known of the mode of action of anaesthetics. However, an industrial scientist, J. Ferguson, was of great help to the chemists working on the problem. He pointed out that most anaesthetics were chemically fairly inert substances and all probably acted as anaesthetics by the same mechanism, with no particular chemical structure being necessary. So, in looking for non-inflammable substitutes for ether, chemists focussed on physical, rather than chemical, properties.

They would need to be, like ether and chloroform, volatile liquids boiling at about 35°C. The class of compounds that the research chemists chose to study were the halogenated hydrocarbons that had been developed for use in refrigerators. These are compounds of carbon and hydrogen in which the hydrogen has been wholly or partly replaced by fluorine, chlorine or bromine. A number of these compounds were prepared and tested for their boiling points, toxicity and inflammability. They were also tested for their anaesthetic properties and adverse side effects, using mice, dogs and rabbits for this purpose.

The formulae and boiling points of some anaesthetics and some of the new compounds that were prepared and tested are listed in the *Glossary*.

Three of the halogenated hydrocarbons considered had similar boiling points and were found to have similar anaesthetic potencies. Two compounds caused severe disturbance to the heart rhythm and were therefore ruled out as possible anaesthetics, but one compound, fluothane, rapidly produced smooth anaesthesia in dogs and did not affect respiration or the normal rhythm of the heart.

When fluothane is administered to patients, they rapidly become unconscious. Their respiration and heart-beat remain normal; their muscles are relaxed and they rarely suffer from any post-operative vomiting, following easy emergence from the state of anaesthesia. This compound is now used extensively in hospitals all over the world.

The work of the chemist did not end until the large-scale manufacture of fluothane had been achieved. Processes first used in the research laboratory may require many modifications or even radical changes. Purification of the required compounds and removal of the by-products also need to be investigated.

The search for new anaesthetics still goes on. The precise mechanism of anaesthetic action presents a challenge to research workers. An understanding of the processes of anaesthesia may lead to the development of other new drugs for the relief of human suffering.

A modern young man with a chill
Thought he'd take a traditional pill.
But alas, when he had,
It tasted so bad
He said: 'I would rather be ill.'

When later he had a bad head
He took modern medicine instead.
When he heard what it cost,
He said 'Oh – I'm lost.
I'll just have to go back to bed!'

G.V.P.

CHAPTER 16: RUBBISH

Better to Use it than to Dump it

IN RETROSPECT, my life's journey seems to have included several experiences of sewage disposal. As a schoolboy, I remember the visit of our class to the local sewage works. At the end of the tour we were offered a glass of clear water that had come out from the treatment plant. Most of us had a sip. I thought, 'What clever people chemists must be!'. Later, when I joined the staff of a residential school in the country, I found that it had its own sewage works. Whether the treated water was added to the boys' water supply I do not know, but I do know that the solid residue was scattered on the meadow where the dairy herd browsed – no doubt to the enrichment of the school milk that we all drank.

When on an Anglo-Norwegian course on Science Teaching held at Nordheim, a lovely village at the top end of Nordford, I was put up in the house of the Mayor and his family. It was a delightful experience. I remember especially the cream desserts made by the mayor's wife and the lovely singing of his daughter after supper. When we applauded and asked for more, Father looked at Mother and said 'Oppvask om morgen' (wash up in the morning) – the only Norwegian phrase that I can remem-

Chapter 8 - The floating tin dredge at work

Chapter 8 - And float off their ores in a foam

Chapter 12 - Starting to grow a crop on waste material

Chapter 12 - You need to mine about 70 tons of rock to get 1 lb of gold

Chapter 12 - Crossing the tank of gold cyanide was a bit eerie

Chapter 12 - If you can pick it up, you can keep it!

Chapter 12 - In a modern Gold mining complex

Chapter 12 - A very different sort of gold mining

Chapter 12 - Arriving in South Africa

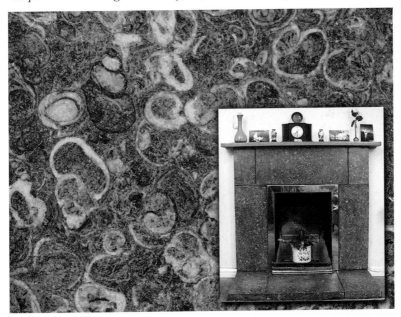

Chapter 9 - Sussex marble used in my fireplace

Chapter 11 - A layer of soda crystals several feet thick

Chapter 14 - Diamond mining leaves big holes in the landscape

Chapter 13 - Casting slabs of crude copper

Chapter 16 - The blast furnaces use charcoal from spent rubber trees

Chapter 17 - Stone Age rock paintings in Lesotho

Chapter 17 - Chemistry by discovery

ber. I also remember the toilets situated in a shed at the end of the garden. They consisted of a long pit, surmounted by a seat with three large holes in it. There was also, I was glad to see, a hole for the guest.

Some years later we built a holiday bungalow in Southern Italy. Made of local limestone and built by a local builder, it was situated near a ruined farmhouse at the upper end of a vineyard sloping down to the village and the one mile of sandy beach – perfect! A soak-away pit was dug a few yards from the house to cope with the sewage. It worked well while we were there, using plenty of water, but when we returned for the next holiday, we found that the pit had dried out and the local lizards were climbing back up to the closet, bringing earth and other livestock with them.

However, this chapter, although you may now be thinking otherwise, is not about sewage. The disposal of the rubbish, produced in enormous quantities by so-called civilised society, causes different, and often more difficult, problems. Apart from putting my kitchen waste on the compost heap in my garden, the empty wine bottles in 'brown, green or clear' holes in the bin for glass at the refuse centre, and the piles of unwanted junk mail and the largely unused copies of *The Times* in the wastepaper bin, I put the rest in the dustbin. From this it is collected and disposed of by the local Council. 'Disposal' consists of re-cycling the plastic and metal and burying the rest in land-fill sites, where it decomposes uselessly and causes future problems when the land is utilized. Let me give you some figures: 27 million tonnes of household rubbish were produced in the UK in 1998, of which only 8% was recycled. The rubbish treated consisted of 4.5 million tonnes of paper, 1.7 of glass, 0.61 of tin, 0.91 of plastic and 0.49 of textiles.

Packaging

One of the more wasteful industries, and one that gives rise to more rubbish than most, must surely be the packaging industry. There is hardly anything one buys that is not already in a close-fitting plastic cover, then put in a polythene bag, and eventually taken away in a paper or plastic container. For transport by post, articles are surrounded by polystyrene chunks in a cardboard container and then wrapped in brown paper. Weekly newspapers, journals and most junk mail are wrapped in polythene. In my view, the industry needs a re-think – and possibly a return from plastic to paper. Although industry can turn polythene bags into wonderfully warm, lightweight, pullovers, one wonders how much of it is re-cycled in this sort of way? However, appropriate packaging is important; one example is described in the chapter on Limestone.

Waste disposal is a problem that civilisation brings with it. In developing countries it is different. When I was in Sarawak, visiting a longhouse built on stilts in which a number of Dyak families live side by side, I observed their method of disposing of kitchen waste etc. The floor of the longhouse is made of planks so lined up that there are gaps of about 1–2 cm between each. The whole longhouse is about six feet above ground level and pigs and dogs move around in the open spaces below the house. I was once entertained to a meal in such a longhouse. I found

the pieces of buffalo meat impossible to chew, so I disposed of the inedible pieces through the gaps in the floor,
no doubt adding to the diet of the animals below.

However, there are other problems of waste disposal
arising in such countries. I have seen dumps of all kinds
of rubbish in all kinds of places. Around the beautiful
islands of Malaysia, plastic and other rubbish is accumu-
lating along the sea-shores. Washed away by the receding
tide, it is returned by the next incoming one. Great wreaths
of such rubbish are becoming an increasing problem to
the shallow-water fishing industry and an eyesore to tourists (tourism is also an important industry). In the last few
years, processes have been developed to dispose of this
sort of refuse and to turn it into useful and marketable
materials. Clearly the emphasis is on 'marketable'; it is
more likely that a process will be adopted if it produces
a saleable product. In changing an industry in the direction
of utilization of waste products or of re-cycling, money is
needed. Once the change is made, it can be economically
advantageous. Among examples of the use of by-products
are the bottling of natural gas that was previously burnt
off at oil wells and the use of surplus heat energy from
power stations to warm adjacent dwellings, as used to be
done at Battersea, London. Another widespread and successful example of re-cycling is the use of ash from solid
fuel, as in power stations, for making building blocks
('breeze blocks') and other insulation material for use in
house building.

I will now describe some processes that I have heard of
recently. In the first, organic waste, i.e. waste consisting
largely of carbon compounds – food waste, plastics, scrap

wood etc, is converted into carbon itself. There is a demand for this, and not only by users of barbecues; in most rural countries it is the main form of fuel, especially for cooking. I also came across a demand for charcoal in the steel industry in Malaysia. Instead of using anthracite coal in the blast furnaces producing iron and steel from low grade ores, an industrial plant that I visited in Butterworth used charcoal obtained from spent rubber trees (*photograph*). This was an integrated process in which the charcoal and ore were the raw materials and steel rods for use in re-inforced concrete were the products.

The process used to convert organic waste to charcoal is a modern form of the charcoal factories of which one sees many in third world countries. Traditionally, some dry wood is burnt and this provides heat for turning the rest of the wood into charcoal, as charcoal burners did in England for centuries. Most furnaces are burning waste wood but in some, trees from valuable forests are burnt. This process has many harmful side effects on the environment but with the modern process, dry wood and organic waste are not burnt but 'toasted', i.e. heated in specially designed ovens to turn the organic compounds into charcoal. Harmful gases such as methane and carbon monoxide are burnt internally to fuel the process without any harmful emissions. I have seen a photograph of a piece of charcoal the same shape as the banana from which it was formed. Such a process, producing a saleable product, could pay for itself if properly developed.

Another process I heard of produces a wood substitute called 'Environ' made from plastic waste. The product is manufactured by an extrusion process and can be produced in various forms and profiles to resemble wood. It is very hard, does not split or fade in colour and is u.v. stable. It does not absorb water and is therefore rot-proof. Its potential as a wood substitute material could contribute seriously to preserving the rain forests, which are being depleted at an alarming rate world-wide. The material is being used as the main structural element for New World housing. It is eminently suitable for this application as it is also resistant to termite and insect damage, which is a serious problem in many parts of the world. It can be manufactured to form many profile shapes, including structural elements, roof rafters and purlins, window-frames, door-frames, floor boards and internal and external cladding. It is an exceptional product which could make a major impact on the environment.

I have very recently read of a specialised development in Malaysia for using the waste that collects below palm oil trees. This is normally burnt off or left to rot on the ground. I have seen tons of oil palm waste rot away in plantations. A seven-year research programme at the University in Penang has produced a durable composite recyclable material suitable for use in the building, furniture and automobile industries. It can be used to make items such as door panels, seat backs and smaller items usually now made from plastics. The technology has been adopted by a local firm, which plans to use waste from 200 oil palm plantations (*The Star*, Malaysia, 24.2.00). The cost will be lower than that of petroleum-based plastic products.

I can imagine that with the increasing interest in caring for the environment there will be many such new processes developed by chemists to make economic use of 'rubbish'.

Another recently developed process is mind-boggling! A major menace to the welfare of our planet is the release into the air of compounds that attack and thin the ozone layer that protects us from receiving overdoses of ultra-violet light. Such stuff consists of compounds of fluorine with hydrocarbons such as are used in the workings of refrigerating machinery and aerosols. These compounds are very stable and extremely difficult to dispose of – until recently. A process is now in use which can do the trick! Is is called 'Plascon' and was developed in Australia for the disposal of hazardous waste. Plascon uses extremely high temperatures to break down the toxic materials, leaving harmless products. The materials include not only fluor-carbons but pesticides, herbicides and other poisonous compounds. They are subjected to very high temperatures, up to 10,000°C or more, which result from large discharges of electricity in an inert gas (such as argon). The superheated cloud of gas or plasma at once breaks down the toxic stuffs into the atoms or ions of which they consist. These are then converted into harmless substances such as common salt. The Plascon plant is conveniently small, about the size of a shipping container. A 150 kilowatt unit can process from 1 to 5 tonnes a day and can be up to 99.999% efficient, depending on the waste being treated. Such units have been in operation since 1995, and in 1998 won the Society of Chemical Industries' award as 'Plant of the Year'.

Atmospheric Pollution and Asthma

Some of our gaseous rubbish goes into the atmosphere

and aggravates the disabilities of sufferers from asthma. Sulphur dioxide, produced by burning sulphur-containing coal and oxides of nitrogen from car exhausts, are the main offenders. Research in Britain shows that 6% of the population suffers from asthma, costing about £50 billion a year in terms of medical care and work hours lost. A lot of this could be saved by a new system of forecasting levels of atmospheric pollution called 'Advanced System of Teledetection for Healthcare Management of Asthma' (ASTHMA). The information could be conveyed to asthma sufferers through mobile phones or the Internet, enabling them to stay indoors on days of high pollution, or wear a gas-mask when they go out. Fortunately, high levels of pollution requiring such drastic remedies are limited to certain crowded cities, such as Tokyo.

Another pollutant is carbon dioxide. This is produced when fossil fuels are burnt and, as we all know, when animals exhale. Plankton in the oceans, exposed to sunlight, consume it as do the green leaves. However, only about a fifth of the earth's forests remains and, since the year 1900 the world's population has increased by a factor of three and the consumption of fossil fuels by a factor of about 30. The percentage of carbon dioxide in the atmosphere has risen by 30% over the past century, presumably because of these two factors. The removal of carbon dioxide from the effluents of a number of industries is an integral part of their activities.

The chemical industry is often accused by the layman of producing poisonous substances and polluting our environment. I hope these examples will show that industrial chemists are not only aware of the dangers inherent in chemical processes (most of which are designed for our benefit) but actively concerned in dealing with any hazardous by-products.

> All rubbish need not go to waste.
> You can process a lot into paste.
> Then extrude (as you could)
> Into flat planks of 'wood'
> Or nice mouldings according to taste.

G.V.P.

CHAPTER 17: IDEAS

Ideas need stuff through which to be expressed

'We are such stuff as dreams are made on'
(William Shakespeare, *The Tempest*)

SITTING IN MY GARDEN early one evening in my new rocking chair made of Iroko wood from Ghana, I had an idea that I thought I would like to introduce into this, my book on Stuff. Knowing how fickle my memory is, I dragged myself out of my chair and moved to my word processor. Under a suitable heading, I typed in my new idea. 'That's that', I thought. But I was wrong. Next day I went to type what I had recorded but, much as I tried, I could not remember what name I had put it under. 'Thought for Stuff', 'New Thought' – I tried everything I could think of without success. So my bright idea had *gone* – I could not recall it. And yet, it was there somewhere, hiding in a minute corner of a silicon chip. Three days later while eating my cornflakes at breakfast the clue popped up from some deep recess in my memory: 'Bright Idea' – of course that was it and I lost no time in recovering it and typing it out. It was a pity I hadn't used those old stuffs, ink and paper, for recording it.

But do 'ideas' justify a place in a book about Stuff?

Central as ideas and thought have been to the development of civilised men, whatever the nature of ideas, they are certainly not 'stuff' with a chemical structure that I can write about. Or are they? The study of the brain has proceeded a long way and we now know what bits are responsible for movement and which for perceiving colour. Perhaps, one day, we shall be able to identify the electrochemical mini-current that corresponds to each and every thought. Even so, I think there is no doubt that, though thoughts and ideas are not stuff, they have a vital connection with it. To be of any consequence, thought must be communicated. From the earliest records, man has communicated his thoughts to others. He has painted on rock surfaces in caves or in the open (*photograph*). He has made signs with his arms and hands; he has clicked with his tongue and slowly developed spoken languages. He has carved hieroglyphs on stone, written words on papyrus, and eventually developed the printing press.

Without some sort of stuff with which to express himself, man's thoughts and ideas would be moribund. What could the author do without writing materials, the sculptor without clay, the painter without canvas and paint, or the musician without a lute or a flute? The one-time poet laureate, Robert Bridges put it better (1929):

'Hast thou then thought that all this ravishing music,
that stirreth so thy heart, making thee dream of things
illimitable, unsearchable and of heavenly import,
is but a light disturbance of the atoms of air,
whose jostling ripples, gathered within the ear, are tuned
to resonant scale, and thence by the enthroned mind received
on the spiral stairway of her audience chamber

as heralds of high spiritual significance?
and that without thine ear, sound would have no report,
nature have no music.'

Stuff plays a bigger part in the communication of men's thoughts, whether they be writers, painters or musicians, than mere transference. The very stuff he uses influences the richness with which he can express his ideas. Think of the improvement in painting materials from the chalk, ochre, charcoal and rust of the caveman in the Dordogne or the aborigine in Australia to the sets of oil paints from Messrs Rowney. Or the development of the violin from the viol or of the piano from the harp.

There seems to be a general belief among musicians that an expert player can modify the performance of a given instrument by playing on it. I asked a young expert violinist, who now restores old and damaged violins such as those of Stradivari (1644–1737), to write down some of his experiences and opinions for me. I could not do better for you, dear readers, than reproduce the essence of what he wrote, for it shows in detail that 'stuff matters to musicians'.

'Artorus Stradivari, the undisputed master of the Cremonese instrument-making tradition, made over 1,000 stringed instruments of which some 640 remain today. They are revered by top soloists but also by collectors and have, in the last 30 years, become unaffordable for any mortal musician.

'Examples of instruments made by Guarnari 'del Gesu' (1698–1744) are also considered by musicians to be of exceptional tonal quality but, in terms of craftsmanship, do not compare to the exactitudes employed by Stradivari.

There are only a few hundred instruments (only violins) made by 'del Gesu' in existence and they are greatly sought after by player and collector.

'What exactly makes instruments from these two makers so desirable and expensive? They are expensive simply through demand. It is clear the demand from musicians originates in the tonal superiority of these makers. And from a collector's point of view, it is easy to understand why someone would wish to own an object of such stunning beauty.

'From about 1735 to the end of his life, in 1744 del Gesu broke away from the restraints of tradition and produced some of the most enigmatic violins ever made. Although he used high quality wood remaining from the family business, his instruments seemed to be of little interest to anyone. They were built with seemingly little precision and had an appearance of being made with haste. He ignored the standard Cremonese measurements of the time, constructing the instruments with a fairly short back length and allowing excessive thicknesses. With the short neck of the time, the low string tension and use of gut strings, it is easy to suppose that these instruments did not sound well. Yet 250 years later some of the top soloists prefer the sound of a del Gesu to that of a Stradivari.

'It is clear the instruments by Stradivari and Guarnari are different in form but also in character. Stradivaris have an exceptionally strong personality in their sound that is allegedly very difficult to override by the instrumentalist. The great Catalonian cellist Pablo Cassals owned a Stradivari cello but rarely performed on it as he found it almost impossible to bring his personality into the music on such an instrument. A del Gesu is the antithesis of this phenomenon. After playing a del Gesu for some 30 minutes, the instrument feels and responds to you as if you have played it your whole life.

'The point which arises from this is that most violins, whether they are Stradivaris, del Gesus, or any other type, seem to adhere tonally to the player. A violinist will generally use one violin for a period of several years or decades and will only reluctantly allow another player to use it, even if it is only for a few minutes. If another violinist plays on it for a few days, when the instrument is back in the owner's hands, he will notice a considerable tonal difference which can be heard by all. After a day or so of playing by the owner, the instrument will slowly revert back to the original sound.'

So it is clear that the conveying of musical ideas from one mind to another is heavily dependent on stuff – in fact that the material of the channel of communication can influence the message. Beethoven's later works are said to owe their greater richness to the development of more sophisticated musical instruments.

I was woken up this morning by music from my CD-radio alarm, a wonderful example of a sophisticated instrument whose invention required a multitude of ideas, some of which date back to discoveries such as that of the electric current and others to later inventions. Electric currents were there already waiting to be discovered by Volta and made use of by Davy and Faraday. Later stuffs, such as silicon chips, were invented by man, not waiting to be discovered – you don't find 'chips' lying around in Silicon Valley.

I have chosen two areas that are more or less familiar

to me, in which the communication of ideas is heavily dependent on stuffs: (i) Music and (ii) Science Education. I have some slight experience of music-making and a lot more than 'slight' experience of science education.

(i) Music

When I was a boy my parents arranged for me to have piano lessons for several years. I was a lazy pupil and did not practise. The result was that the only 'piece' I could play was the last one I had learnt. However, I acquired a sense of rhythm that was to stand me in good stead later, when I was to conduct a small amateur orchestra performing Gilbert & Sullivan operettas.

I first came to enjoy the music of Gilbert and Sullivan through the enthusiasm of my best friend at school, Dick Turnbull. When the D'Oyly Carte Opera Company was in London, we queued for seats in the gallery of the Princes Theatre as often as we could – our record was 9 times in a fortnight. Dick was a Gilbert and Sullivan purist and objected to any talking during the overtures. His loud 'shush', however, only added to the disturbance.

While teaching science at Christ's Hospital, I used to take small groups of boys 'geologising' in the Malvern Hills. One evening, as we walked down the last slopes, I burst into song – a bit of Gilbert and Sullivan's *Trial by Jury*. That evening, over the glowing embers of the farm's wood fire, we sang much of the whole operetta. During the next school term a few enthusiasts persuaded me (without much difficulty!) to produce *Trial by Jury* at the school. A year later, this was followed by *HMS Pinafore*.

Our orchestra was made up of members of the teaching staff and older boys. The clarinetist was a boy named Colin Davis, now Sir Colin and a world-famous conductor. The cellist did not become famous; in fact he was the source of some embarrassing moments. He was a delightful, but very short-sighted colleague. He sat close to his music stand, peering at the score through his thick glasses and apparently oblivious to what was going on around him. Towards the end of the first act of *HMS Pinafore* there is a silence broken by the entry of a cello, but in rehearsals it never came in. 'We had better compare your score with mine', I said. So we worked through from the beginning of the last chorus. At the bottom of a page of the cello score was a figure 12. 'Then you have 12 bars rest', I said. 'Oh', said the dear cellist, 'is that a 12? I've never noticed it before – I wondered why I got to the end of the act and everyone else was still playing.'

My trumpeter was very professional. He read his copy of the school magazine until a few bars before he was due to play his few notes, put it down in good time and resumed reading it after playing his part. He later became Professor of English Literature at Oxford University.

An old man, who played the French Horn,
Had only three notes to perform.
When awaiting his cue,
Someone shouted out YOU
But his moment had then come and gorn.

G.V.P.

(I wrote this limerick specially for the BBC's Radio 3 and am happy to say that they broadcast it.)

When the boys involved in our production of Gilbert & Sullivan left school, they formed a society and we continued with our productions. We performed *The Pirates of Penzance* in the school theatre and *Iolanthe* and *The Yeomen of the Guard* in the theatre of the Guildhall School of Music during subsequent years.

(ii) Research and Science Education

Progress in scientific research depends largely on someone having a new idea. I have already referred to the well-known example in the history of chemistry of Kekulé's vision of the structure of the benzene molecule (see Chapter 4). It is said that he was riding on a tram, thinking about molecules consisting of chains of carbon atoms. They were wriggling about like serpents. Then, as he watched them in his imagination, one of the serpents got hold of its own tail in its mouth. The carbon chain became a ring – and the idea of a ring structure for the benzene molecule was born. I have described another example where thinking up ideas was an integral part of the research for a new drug for Migraine (Chapter 15).

The history of Physics could be regarded as the history of ideas about the nature of substances. Ideas lead to further experimental investigation and new knowledge, which, in turn, leads to new theories (or ideas). J.J. Thomson, Professor of Physics at the Cavendish Laboratory, Cambridge, must be credited with ideas that led to the discovery of the electron. He was a genius. The following description is taken from *The Dons* by Noel Annan. He describes how a researcher working in the Cavendish was reduced to despair when the apparatus he had built failed to function.

'Along would shuffle this remarkable being, who, after cogitating in a characteristic attitude over his funny old desk in the corner, and jotting down a few figures and formulae in his tidy handwriting on an old envelope, would produce a luminous suggestion, like a rabbit out of a hat, not only revealing the cause of the trouble, but also the means of cure. This intuitive ability to comprehend the inner working of intricate apparatus without the trouble of handling it appeared to me then, and still appears to me now, as something verging on the miraculous, the hallmark of great genius.'

Yes, he was certainly a genius who could manipulate in his head ideas concerning stuffs. Before formulating his theory of the structure of the atom, he must have had the idea that was the basis of it.

This process of observing phenomena, followed by the formulation of a theory to explain them, followed in turn by experiments to test the theory (traditionally known as the 'scientific method') should form an important element in the process of education. It is the basis of the 'discovery method' in science teaching and is in contrast with the 'didactic' method, in which pupils are told what to learn. A Chinese teacher I know described the latter method by saying: 'Confucius he say – and you ruddy well learn it.'

When discussing teaching, I am always reminded of Alfred, a character in a book by the Australian author, Paul White: 'I dunno', said Alfred, 'I've forgotten all I was taught. I only remember what I learnt.' As one of my brightest ex-pupils said to me, when we met many years after he left school: 'Don't think you ever taught me anything – don't be upset, no-one has ever taught anyone anything – you can take a horse to the water but you can't make him drink.' This influenced my attitude thereafter and when I was lecturing to future science teachers, I always told them of this episode. They would retort: 'If we can't teach, what should we do as teachers?' 'Your job,' I would reply, 'is to do all you can to help your pupils to learn, to stimulate their interest, encourage them to want to know and understand more, provide them with the facilities to do it, and be there to encourage, explain and help, and finally give tests to enable them to identify their weak points.'

This method of teaching, known as the Discovery Method, emphasises learning, not teaching. It dates back to H.E. Armstrong's 'Heuristic' method. The word comes from the Greek word 'eureka' – 'I have found it' (which Archimedes said as he discovered that when he got into his full bath, an equal volume of water got out). Critics of Armstrong say that it is absurd to expect school pupils to discover all they are expected to learn. Of course it is, but this is a gross distortion of what Armstrong envisaged. He entrusted the trying out of his method to a science teacher at Christ's Hospital in the early 19th century named Charles E. Browne. Armstrong often visited the school and was picturesquely described by the headmaster of the time as follows:

'Our first science master, Charles E. Browne, was a pioneer in Armstrong's heuristic method and successfully

~168~

solved the difficult problem of applying it in practice to a school of over 800 pupils. At first, most of the other teachers looked loftily askance at Browne, but it was not long before the infection of the virus heuristicum *Armstrongii* had been spread to other subjects. Teachers began to abandon the belief that textbooks and their own voices were the only methods of teaching and to devise ways in which pupils could take an active part. Armstrong took a lively, paternal interest in all these developments. He visited us often, usually wearing those loose tweeds, dyed, rumour said, by his own hand (by means of vegetable dyes of course) to a colour between that of an orange and a lemon. I always welcomed the sight of his stocky, bearded figure in this characteristic costume.'

I was lucky enough to be one of Browne's students when studying for my Diploma in Education at London University, and even luckier to succeed him as Head of Science at Christ's Hospital. Here I tried to adapt the heuristic ideas to a modern situation: we had bigger classes, less time and more pressure from examinations than Browne had.

In 1949 I published a textbook called *Chemistry by Discovery* which encapsulated the spirit of Armstrong's heuristic method. This later influenced the teaching of science through the Nuffield Science Teaching Project, and, to some extent, through the National Curriculum.

The following example will illustrate how these ideas worked out in practice with a chemistry class.

'What's this black stuff, sir?' 'Don't you know? What do you think it is? No idea?' When teaching chemistry (or any other subject) the teacher can either say: 'Here are the facts – you learn them and next week I'll test you', or he can say: 'Here's an interesting thing – let's find out more about it'.

I used to start my junior chemistry lessons by giving the class a few substances to heat (*photograph*) – chosen so that something visible would happen. I always included a piece of shiny copper foil. When heated it 'goes black'. 'Has it changed colour or is that black stuff on its surface?' 'I can scrape it off – it must be stuff.' 'I wonder how it got there? – any ideas?' Smith says: 'I think it's soot from the flame'. 'Good idea' – I write it on the board. 'Smith's theory – the black stuff is soot.' 'He may be right,' I say. 'Any other ideas?' 'Yes, sir,' says Robinson, 'I think it's an impurity driven out of the copper by the heat.' So Robinson's theory goes up on the board too. 'I know what it is,' says Solly, whose older brother is in the Fifth Form. 'If you know, you will have to prove you are right – we'll add it to our theories.' Solly's theory: 'the black stuff is formed by the air acting on the copper.' 'How shall we decide who is right?,' I ask. I get them to suggest experiments to test the three theories. 'Heat it away from the air, sir.' With various classes I have heated copper foil under sand, under water, in steam, sealed in the glass of a test tube and under molten salt. Apart from the sand, all keep the air off the copper and it does not go black. 'Smith's theory must be wrong,' rings out from the class. Robinson tested his theory by heating his piece of copper for a long time – he even came in after hours but the copper never seemed to be rid of the black stuff – there was just more of it. Poor old Robinson!

We rigged up a tube from which the air could be removed by a pump so that Solly could heat his piece of copper in a vacuum and see what happened when air was absent. When it was in the vacuum, the copper, although red hot, remained bright. Then came the big moment – Solly opened the tap to admit air and immediately the colour of the copper changed to black. We once made a film called *Exploring Chemistry*. There is a never-to-be-forgotten close-up of Solly, cautiously smiling and saying: 'I think my theory must be right, sir.'

Yes, ideas, however bright, need materials to establish their truth or falsehood. 'What is truth?,' asked jesting Pilate. One might have replied: 'Truth is an ever-expanding body of experimentally verifiable theories.' A scientist's theories may explain known facts at a certain time but the discovery of further facts may require the theory to be modified. It was not wrong at the time: it was just proved later to be inadequate. Present theories are stepping stones to further knowledge. As long as we go on 'having ideas', we shall go on modifying what we believe to be 'the truth' – but maybe never reaching it.

Karl Popper, the 20th century philosopher, quotes the painter Dürer, writing in the 15th century: 'I shall let the little I have learnt go forth into the day in order that someone better than I may guess the truth and in his work may prove and rebuke my error. At this I shall rejoice that I was yet the means whereby this truth has come to light.' I once saw the statue of Dürer in Nuremberg. It was just a year after the town had been reduced to rubble in World War II. The statue stood proudly above a mound of charred wood and twisted iron. A small boy was risking his safety as he tried to salvage some wood. Dürer looked down unscathed.

We live in a world made of stuff.
I've already said more than enough.
To get understanding
Is very demanding
And will use up a lot of your 'puff'.

G.V.P.

When Longfellow, in his *Psalm of Life*, quoted the well-known lines from the Bible about 'dust' ('Dust thou art, to dust returneth') he might have said:

Stuff thou art, to stuff returneth,
Was not spoken of the soul.

After such thoughts I found that I enjoyed listening to Tchaikovsky's triumphal 1812 Overture and Beethoven's setting of Schiller's *Ode to Joy*, the last movement of the 9th Symphony. And, above all, Brahms' Intermezzo 117, which I like to call 'Meditations on Stuff'.

EPILOGUE

Who was this Chemist?

I WOKE AT 4 a.m. on my sixth birthday to look at the presents at the foot of my bed. A chemistry set! Did that start my interest in science? There is no doubt that chemistry became my favourite subject at school. The changes brought about by chemical reactions intrigued me – and still do. A lot of school children choose chemistry for this reason. There are exciting colours, smells and bangs and mysterious changes of one substance into another. There is a magic in chemistry. Later, at university level, chemistry becomes more mathematical and students find it quite tough. Some lose interest altogether. The subject becomes more theoretical, striving to explain the mysterious chemical changes in terms of even more mysterious changes – changes in the bonds between atoms, in the excitation of electrons, and other concepts that have no colour or smell and do not go bang. There are many ways in which chemistry has since impinged on my life: at school and university, in teaching school chemistry, during wartime, and in wider interests such as mining, mineralogy and metallurgy.

The only chemical event that I can recall from my junior school days was when Miss Aird (I think that was her name) gave us a piece of coke and some copper sulphate to take home. We were to dissolve the copper sulphate in water and suspend the coke in it from a piece of cotton. After a day or two beautiful blue crystals began to appear on the surface of the coke. This so impressed me that I am sure it gave rise to a lifelong interest in crystals.

After I had taken my B.Sc. examination, I decided to spend a year in research. My Professor, F.G. Donnan, asked me to apply for a grant from the Department of Scientific and Industrial Research. The form stated that the applicant must intend to pursue a career 'in which research plays an integral part'. I wanted to teach, so I thought I could not sign the form. However, that was not Professor Donnan's view: 'If research does not play a part in teaching', he said, 'it certainly should'. So I signed the form – but did not get the grant.

I did a year's research at University College, London, under a very keen young lecturer, Bryan Topley, who was a fine example of a dedicated research worker. We observed no hours; we broke off to play fives together; we stayed on late in the evening; sometimes we had a supper of scrambled eggs at J. Lyons & Co in Tottenham Court Road before going home, maybe after 10 p.m. Topley eventually became Managing Director of the large chemical firm, Albright and Wilson. The research itself intrigued me but was of no possible use or interest to anyone else. Some challenging practical skills were involved and I took lessons in glass-blowing. I received helpful hints from a Junior Lecturer, Charles Goodeve. He was a very friendly Canadian and later, as Sir Charles Goodeve FRS, he became Director of Scientific Research during the War and, after it, Director of the British Iron and Steel Federation.

One year's research led nowhere, so my father sent me to continue doing research at Cambridge University for a Ph. D., which required another two years. At that time the regulations for this were such that, on paper, it was logically impossible for anyone outside Cambridge to be accepted as a research student. First, you had to find a supervisor willing to take you on as a research student – but he could not do this unless a College had accepted you. No College would accept you unless you had a research supervisor. Anywhere other than Cambridge (and maybe Oxford), this problem would have been insoluble, but all I had to do to solve it was to spend a day walking from the College (Emmanuel) to the laboratories and to the Registry and back several times, and in a few hours the whole thing was settled.

I was lucky in my supervisor, Professor (later Sir Eric) Rideal. He became the first occupant of the Chair of Colloid Science. He visited each of his research students almost daily. Holding his little curly pipe, he was always encouraging if things were stagnating or going wrong, and had a merry twinkle in his eye if things looked good. He was an inspiring but often incomprehensible lecturer, covering the board at all angles and in all spare corners with almost illegible handwriting. Unlike most lecturers these days, he liked to do some simple demonstration experiment during the course of his lecture – I'm sure he knew that after 20 or 30 minutes the attention of his audience needed recalling.

I was fortunate to be in Cambridge while the great

pioneers in atomic physics were still around. Lord Rutherford, Sir J. J. Thomson and others were men who made fundamental contributions to our understanding of the structure of atoms. Their names will always be remembered by future generations for the key roles they and other British scientists played in opening up the world of atomic physics and nuclear energy.

My recollections of these famous physicists are not only of their scientific but also of their human qualities. I remember seeing Sir J. J. Thomson, once Cavendish Professor of Physics, discoverer of the electron, staring into an antique shop, his hands behind his back, his over-long trousers frayed at the turn-ups, his bowler hat well back on his head and his ill-fitting false teeth giving him a perpetual smile. By this time he was Master of Trinity College and had been succeeded at the Cavendish Laboratory by Sir Ernest, later Lord, Rutherford.

Rutherford was world famous for his experiments in atomic disintegration and for his nuclear theory of the structure of the atom. I remember being asked by a visitor from overseas what the building we were facing was? When I said it was the Cavendish Laboratory, he took off his hat and said; 'Not where the great Lord Rutherford works?' I went to a few of Rutherford's lectures. His notes were written on a bunch of little cards, which he invariably dropped on the lecture bench sooner or later and thereby got into a muddle. In the end it became a gimmick and he did it deliberately – or so we believed. There are many stories about him. One concerns the occasion when he showed his students two little bottles containing samples of the two isotopes of mercury sent to him by a Danish scientist. They were identical except that their densities differed by a few parts per million. 'I would be obliged if any of you can think of a way of demonstrating this small difference.' One of the students put the problem to Dr Searle, an ingenious experimental physicist in the Cavendish. Relations between Searle and Rutherford were cool, and when, a few days later, they met in the corridor, Searle said: 'I hear you want to demonstrate the difference in density of two samples of mercury?' Rutherford replied 'Yes. Got any ideas?' To which Searle retorted: 'Put one on the other and see which floats.' (Perhaps I should add that although a cork will float on water because it is less dense, it is absurd to suggest that a light oil will float on a heavy oil – they will first mix together. It would be the same with two samples of mercury.)

Probably one of my most memorable experiences was to attend a lecture by Rutherford in the Royal Institution on the centenary of Mendeleyev's birth. Mendeleyev was the scientist who, in the 1860's, had classified the elements by arranging them in a pattern based on the weights of their atoms. This arrangement was called the Periodic Table of Elements. Elements of similar properties came together in the Table, and before an unknown element was discovered, Mendeleyev could predict its properties. At the time there was no explanation of why these regularities should exist, but when Rutherford enunciated his theory of the structure of the atom, all became clear. It was exciting to hear Rutherford himself describe how this was so – what a pity Mendeleyev could not be there to hear it!

During my time at Cambridge, the Master of Christ's

College was a scholarly biologist, Sir Arthur Shipley. His textbook *Life* must be one of the most attractive biology books ever written. Packed with quotations from literature, every topic from life to death is enlivened by apt examples. It was said that Sir Arthur wrote the book in the evenings over a glass of port, sitting in his study in the Master's Lodge and never having to leave his chair to look up a quotation. These all came out of his richly stocked memory. Who could resist reading when each page might hold another gem? 'Many have attempted to define Life. At school they used to tell me that a verb indicated "being, doing or suffering", and this certainly describes life, though it does not define it. Then there is the well known character who defined it as "one damned thing after another", but he was referring to a span of life – "brief life is here our portion". 'Life in the sea is summed up in the conjugation of the French verb "manger" – je mange, tu manges, il mange etc, and its terrible correlative: je suis mangé, tu es mangé, il est mangé etc.' The insect world seemed fascinating when he described it: 'The July bug has wings of gold, the June bug wings of flame, the bed bug has no wing at all but it gets there just the same.'

When Cockroft and Walton first split the atom, I was still a research student at Cambridge. One day in 1931 when my colleagues and I were drinking tea in the university Laboratory of Physical Chemistry, a lightning flash from the Cavendish Laboratory next door interrupted us. It turned out to be a discharge of a million volts from Cockroft and Walton's room next door. A few years later they had succeeded in splitting the atom for the first time. Lord Rutherford had split light atoms by bombarding them with high energy particles emitted from radioactive elements like uranium, but Cockroft and Walton had used missiles they had energised in the laboratory. Their room at the Cavendish was fairly large and the tall structure reaching to the ceiling was the million-volt tube in which they produced high energy protons. At the bottom end of the tube was a small microscope. The room was darkened and when our eyes had got accustomed to the darkness, we looked down the microscope and were told to watch for a small faint flash. After a few minutes I saw one – it was only just visible but it was energy released when a high speed proton hit a lithium atom and formed two alpha particles or helium ions with the release of atomic energy. The next day the daily papers produced headlines like: 'Atom smashed – the Queen Mary can cross the Atlantic on a pinch of salt.' I was sceptical: 'It's only a flash in a microscope that you can hardly see,' I thought.

More than a dozen years passed and World War II was raging. I was going home from work in the Admiralty and passing through Trafalgar Square when – imagine my amazement – I read the *Evening Standard* placards: 'Atomic Bomb Exploded'. This was August 7th 1945. It seemed incredible to me then, and still does, that it had become possible to use the energy obtained when atoms are disintegrated. All credit to the scientists and engineers who, starting from those minute flashes, achieved the colossal feat of chemical and physical engineering that produced atomic energy on a large scale.

Owing to the contributions of scientists such as these, we know a lot more about the structure of matter now than was known in the 19th century. Great scientists, both men and women, are to be found today, whose work builds on that of the people I have mentioned. Chemists are at the forefront in unravelling the mysteries of living systems and in the creation of new drugs and materials. Chemists are concerned with stuff of all kinds.

I taught Chemistry at Christ's Hospital for about 30 years. When the Headmaster, H.L.O. Flecker, retired, he accepted the post of Principal of Lawrence College in Pakistan. Unknown to him, this opened up for me a new series of 'Encounters with Stuff'! After he had been at Lawrence College a year, he wrote to me about their laboratories: 'They are not bad, but the Bunsen burners don't work'. He wanted me to go out and help his science staff to get things going properly. The British Council paid my fare and the Fleckers put me up in their white painted wooden house on a slight rise overlooking the school. This was my first visit to Asia and my reactions on arrival at the Customs were, shall we say, naive. The Fleckers had asked me to bring out certain groceries difficult to obtain in Pakistan: Marmite, Bovril, Jacob's water biscuits, Chivers jelly, creams etc. I duly entered these in detail on the customs declaration form. 'What is this Marmeet?' asked the Customs officer. 'And Chivers – who is he?' Soon he gave up, tore up the form, gave me another and said: 'Write "Personal Effects"'. Later, when I had my first attack of 'gyppy tummy', I was glad of the Marmite and water biscuits – the only nourishment I felt able to take.

This visit led to the encounter with stuff described in chapter 7 (Limestone). It also led to several other such visits on behalf of the British Council, including those to Iraq, Iran, East Africa and Malaysia and further encounters, e.g.

with petroleum, palm oil, copper and tinstone (see chapters 4, 8 and 13).

The British Council courses on chemistry teaching were intended to help the teachers to update their work and to give them new and exciting ideas. On the whole they failed, largely because teachers were tied to existing syllabuses, textbooks, equipment and tradition. To depart from these was difficult for them. So the Nuffield Foundation thought up a new idea: 'Curriculum Development Projects'. The title almost speaks for itself. It was important that the local Ministries of Education were involved so that the factors that were inhibiting change could be faced and dealt with.

I was fortunate to be asked to coordinate the first such Project – the East Africa Secondary School Science Project. Beginning in 1967, this Project attempted to help Kenya, Tanzania and Uganda work together to improve their school science. In so doing I travelled a lot in East Africa and this certainly widened my understanding of the role of chemistry in life there.

About a year later, a similar Project was begun in Malaysia. Together with a team of six science teachers from the UK, I visited Malaysia twice a year for about eight years. There were, of course, many opportunities to encounter the stuffs for which Malaysia is known – rubber, oil and tin.

Science teachers in Australia and New Zealand had heard of the Nuffield Science Teaching Project and wanted to know more about it. A group of headmasters invited me to go on a tour of 12 centres there and give talks and exhibits on Nuffield Science.

These and other travels contributed to the encounters with stuff which have been described in the preceding chapters.

GLOSSARY

THE FOLLOWING SYMBOLS represent the atoms of elements mentioned in the text:

Ag	Silver	H	Hydrogen
Al	Aluminium	I	Iodine
As	Arsenic	K	Potassium
Au	Gold	Mg	Magnesium
Br	Bromine	N	Nitrogen
C	Carbon	Na	Sodium
Cl	Chlorine	O	Oxygen
Cu	Copper	S	Sulphur
F	Fluorine	Si	Silicon
Fe	Iron	Sn	Tin

The chemical formulae of substances referred to in the text

Chemists represent the internal structure of substances by writing capital letters for the atoms of elements, e.g. O for oxygen, H for hydrogen etc, and linking them up to show the formula of the whole structure of molecules.

In complex molecules the atomic symbols are sometimes omitted, e.g. H and C in the molecules of some organic compounds such as benzene.

Chapter 1: Ink

Food Black II

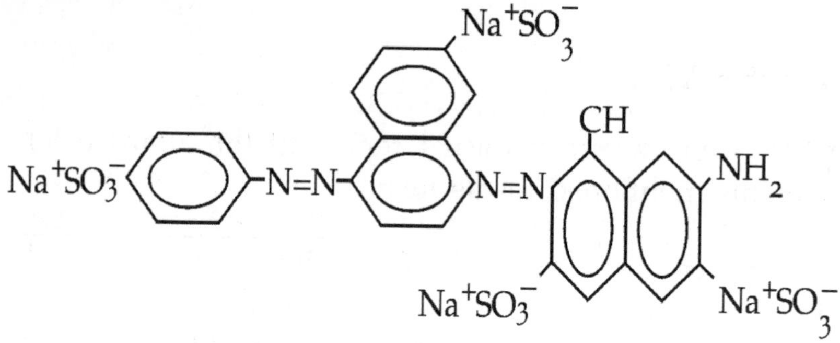

Ink Jet Black

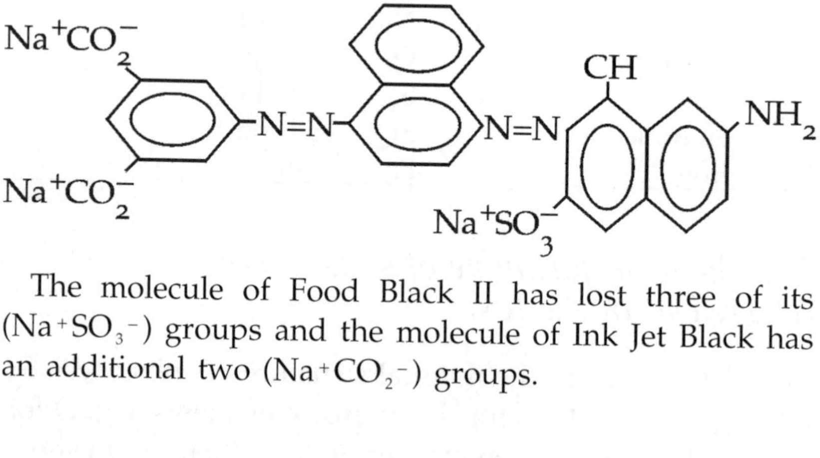

The molecule of Food Black II has lost three of its
$(Na^+SO_3^-)$ groups and the molecule of Ink Jet Black has
an additional two $(Na^+CO_2^-)$ groups.

Chapter 2: Paper

Cellulose consists of long-chain molecules made up of the following units joined together in large numbers. Note that the C for carbon atoms has been omitted where it is part of a ring structure, i.e.

Stands for

Cellulose Unit

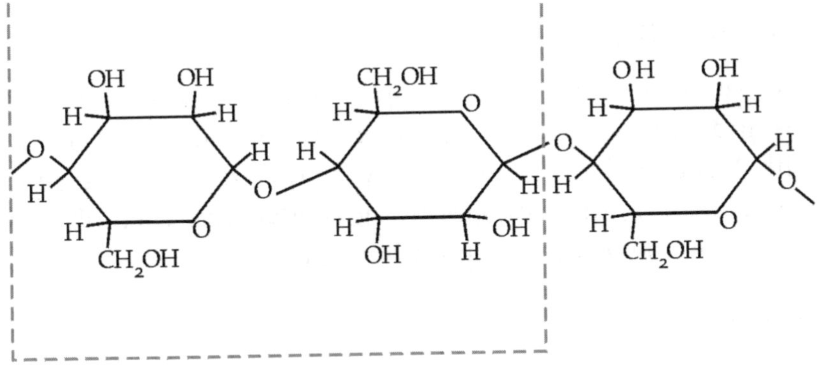

Repeat unit

Chapter 4: Oil

Mineral Oils

Paraffin oils

e.g. $CH_3-CH_2-CH_2 ----- CH_3$

Some include a degree of 'unsaturation' and have formulae such as:

$CH_3-CH_2-CH=CH-CH_2-CH_2 ----- CH_3$

Vegetable Oils

The molecules are more complex than those of mineral oils and consist of combinations of a molecule of glycerine with three molecules of a 'fatty acid'. For example in a molecule of palm oil one molecule of glycerine is combined with three molecules of palmitic acid.

Palmitic Acid

$HO_2C-(CH_2)_{14}-CH_3$

Glycerine

CH_2-OH

$CH-OH$

CH_2-OH

Palm Oil

$$CH_2-O_2C-(CH_2)_{14}-CH_3$$

$$CH-O_2C-(CH_2)_{14}-CH_3$$

$$CH_2-O_2C-(CH_2)_{14}-CH_3$$

This molecule has been formed by eliminating three molecules of water from one molecule of glycerine and three molecules of palmitic acid.

Oleic Acid

$$HO_2C-(CH_2)_7-CH=CH-(CH_2)_7-CH_3$$

Olive Oil

One molecule of glycerine plus three molecules of oleic acid minus three molecules of water, as in the formation of palm oil.

Benzene

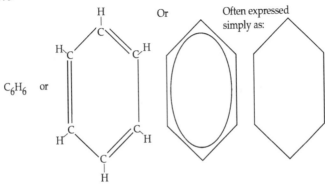

Chapter 6: Food

Alcohol (ethanol)

$C_2H_5.OH$ $CH_3.CH_2.OH$

Sugar

Glucose $C_6H_{12}O_6$

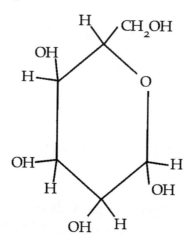

Starch

$(C_6H_{10}O_5)_n$

When starch reacts with water, it forms glucose:-

$(C_6H_{10}O_5)_n + nH_2O \rightarrow nC_6H_{12}O_6$

Amino Acids

The building blocks of proteins.

General Formula:

R= hydrocarbon group

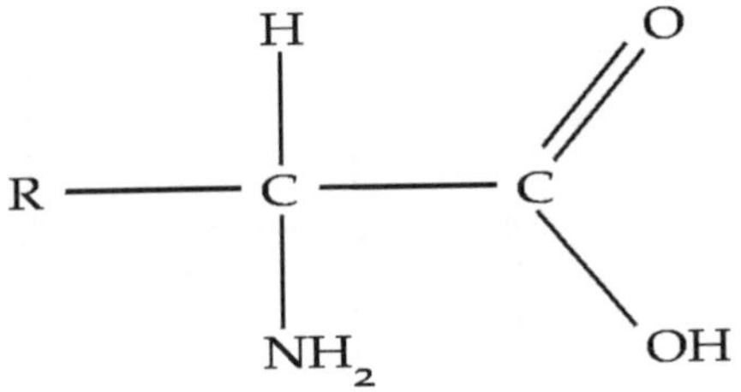

Most of the natural amino acids are of the above form, where R may be one of many groups – e.g. $CH_3 - CH_2$, $C_6 H_5$, $CH_2 OH$, etc.

Example: Glycine

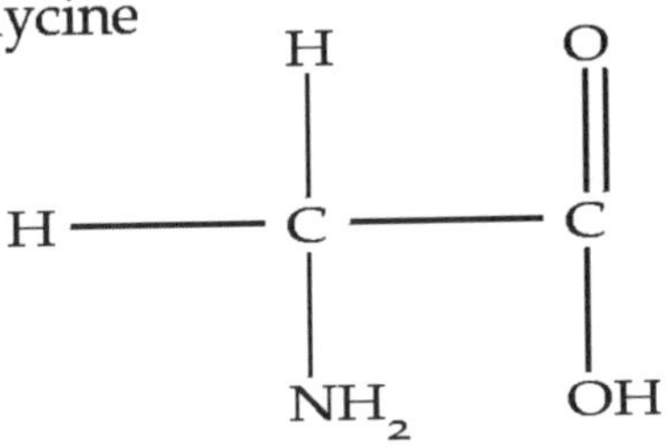

Proteins

Made up of chains of amino acid molecules:

Peptide Chain:

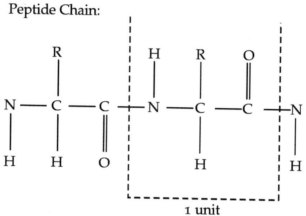

1 unit

There may be hundreds of units in a protein molecule.

Limestone

Calcite $CaCO_3$

Water containing carbon dioxide reacts with calcite rendering it soluble:-

$$CaCO_3 + CO_2 + H_2O \rightleftharpoons Ca(HCO_3)_2 \text{ (soluble)}$$

when the water evaporates calcite is re-formed.

Pyrites FeS_2

Under the action of air and water, it becomes iron sulphate (green vitriol)

$$FeS_2 +3O_2 +H_2O \qquad \rightarrow \qquad \underline{FeSO_4} +H_2SO_3$$

Green vitriol crystals have the formula $FeSO_4\ 7H_2O$

Oil of Vitriol (Sulphuric acid) is formed when green vitriol is heated:

$$2FeSO._4\ 7H_2O \qquad \rightarrow \qquad \underline{2H_2SO_4}\ 2FeO+5H_2O$$
(FeO exidises in the air to $Fe_2O_{,3}$ 'rust')

Chapter 8: Granite

The three principal minerals of which a typical granite is formed are:-

Quartz (Silica) SiO_2

Felspar (e.g. orthoclase, K. Al. Si_3O_8)

Ferromagnesium minerals (e.g. Mica) – Biotite, a common mica, is $K(Mg.\ Fe)(AlSi_3)O_{10}\ (OH.F)_{,2}$ in which the proportions of Mg and Fe and of OH and F. may vary.

The micas have a "sheet" structure based on a series of units of (Si_4O_{10}) in which each silicon atom is joined to 4 oxygen atoms. The sheets are separated by potassium ions as shown in this over-simplified diagram of a short section of a sheet:

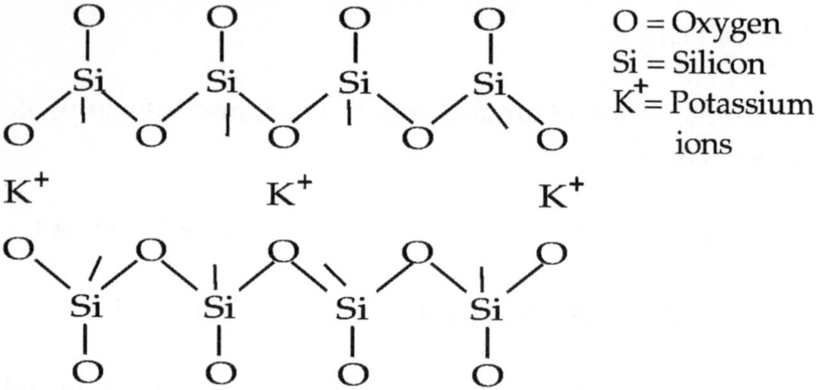

$$
\begin{array}{cccc}
O & O & O & O \\
| & | & | & | \\
Si & Si & Si & Si \\
\end{array}
$$

O   O   O   O

K^+ K^+ K^+

O   O   O   O

Si   Si   Si   Si

O   O   O   O

O = Oxygen
Si = Silicon
K^+ = Potassium ions

When a cross-section of the mica gets damp, the potassium is hydrolysed to form potash, an electrical conductor:

$K^+ + H_2O \rightarrow KOH + H^+$

Chapter 13: Copper

The action of the metal iron in displacing copper from solutions containing compounds of copper is shown by this equation:

$Fe + Cu^{2+} \rightarrow Cu + Fe^{2+}$

Chapter 15: Medicines

Salvarsan

Azo dyes The group of atoms that gives the colour to azo dyes is:-

A typical example is the dye 'Orange II':-

The formula of Arsphenamine ('Salvarsan') is:-

Aspirin

Salicylic Acid

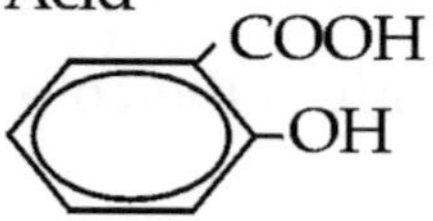

Aspirin

Dispersible (Soluble) Aspirin

Anaesthetics

		Boiling Point °C
Ether	$CH_3.O.CH_3$	35
Chloroform	$CHCl_3$	67
Chloroethane	$CH_3.CH_2Cl$	12.3

New compounds tested as anaesthetics:

		Boiling Point °C
	(i) $CF_2Br.CHFCl$	52
	(ii) $CF_2Cl.CHFBr$	50
Fluothane	(iii) $CF_3.CHBrCl$	50

Drugs for Migraine
"5HT"

"5HT-like"

REFERENCES

Encyclopaedia Britannica

Chemistry and Industry Journals 1998 – 2000

Magic molecules: how drugs work. Susan Aldridge. Cambridge University Press 1998

'Plascon' Plant of the Year. Society of Chemical Industry 1998

'Space-age Soot. Science and Technology.' *The Economist.* 11.12.99

Paper – Parchment. World Book Inc. 1999

The Making of the Chemist: the Social History of Chemistry in Europe. 1789–1914, ed. Knight and Krague. Cambridge University Press 1998

Sir Joseph Banks, Botanist by Benjamin West. *National Geographic.* Nov. 1994

The Chemical Industry – waving not drowning. Chemistry & Industry. 19.10.98

Drip Irrigation. S Dasberg. Agricultural Research Organisation. Bet Dogon, Israel

'Seeing it Through' – Travels of a Science Teacher. Gordon Van Praagh. 1988.

INDEX

*The miracles **of** science*™